The
Secret
Lives
of
Molecules

For Matthew May

First published in Great Britain in 2023 by
Greenfinch
An imprint of Quercus Editions Ltd
Carmelite House
50 Victoria Embankment
London EC4Y 0DZ

An Hachette UK company

Publisher: Kerry Enzor
Project editor: Anna Southgate
Design: Luke Bird
Illustrations: Jo Parry
Picture credits: Stick-and-ball molecules: pp. 33, 41, 53, 61, 65, 69, 77, 81, 85, 89, 93, 97, 105, 113, 117, 121, 129, 132, 145, 153, 157, 165, 169, 173, 177, 181, 193, 197, 205 Liliya/Alamy Stock Vector; p. 17 anchalee thaweeboon/Shutterstock; p. 101 chromatos/Shutterstock.

A CIP catalogue record for this book is available from the British Library

HB ISBN 978-1-52942-509-3
eBook ISBN 978-1-52942-508-6

10 9 8 7 6 5 4 3 2 1

Typeset in Bill Corporate Narrow and Adobe Garamond Pro
Printed and bound in China by C&C Offset Printing Co. Ltd.

Papers used by Greenfinch are from well-managed forests and other responsible sources.

The
Secret
Lives
of
Molecules

Kathryn
Harkup

greenfinch

Contents

Introduction

The periodic table is the basic menu of ingredients for everything around us. We interact with many of the 118 elements listed on it every day, but we know very few of them as individuals. The elements are more often found joined up and clustered together. They can be combined, connected and mixed into an incredible number of different arrangements to give us the variety of molecules that make us and the world around us.

A molecule is a combination of atoms bonded together in a particular way, just as a word is a collection of characters in a specific arrangement. Both are constructed from a limited set of components, either elements or letters. And both take on properties and significance greater than the sum of their parts.

The first step to reading words is learning the alphabet and the first step to reading a molecule is learning about its atoms. At its heart, every atom has a nucleus of protons that defines that element's identity. Neutrons are also squeezed into the nucleus to hold the protons in place. The body of the atom is swelled out by electrons, one for each proton. It is the electrons that give an atom its personality. They shimmer around the nucleus in well-ordered shells, each with a fixed capacity. If there are more electrons than spaces in the shell, a new shell is formed. A self-content atom is an atom with a set of full shells. But most atoms have a few gaps or extras in their outermost shell and these spoil an atom's otherwise neat structure.

At its simplest level, chemistry is the negotiation between atoms to swap, share, donate and acquire electrons to complete their outermost shell, or at least to give the appearance of a complete shell. The exchange of electrons between atoms forms bonds between them and holds them together. The nature of those bonds can vary depending on the strength of an element's personality and negotiating skills.

Some elements can offload unwanted electrons with ease and others in need of electrons can persuade almost any other element to relinquish them. If two of these extreme types meet, electrons are handed from one to the other and everyone is happy. The atoms that lose electrons become positively charged, and those that gain electrons become negatively charged. Opposites attract and the atoms align themselves in regular repeating arrays of positive and negative to make ionic compounds. But not all elements are so forceful in their behaviour. If one atom is less willing to give up its electrons, and its potential partner cannot persuade it to do so, the two can come to a discrete arrangement between themselves and share. Their outermost shells can overlap and the electrons they contain can buzz around both atoms giving the impression of completeness. Such like-minded elements share common interests to form covalent bonds.

Covalent and ionic bonding are the two main ways atoms can get together, but there is a full spectrum of atomic partnerships that fall between these two extremes. Transfers may not be complete and electrons might not be shared equally. These subtleties make all the difference to a molecule. Just as accented letters give emphasis to portions of a word, electrons clustered around or absent from some regions of a molecule are the focus of chemical interest.

The redistribution of electrons around a molecule offers a compromise for the atoms of the elements it contains. The changes to the electrons in its shells change an element's behaviour. Once excitable atoms can be tamed and others invigorated. Individual identities become blurred and merge with others just as particular groupings of letters lose their individual sounds to create a new one.

For both words and molecules, the physical arrangement of their components is important: a pea is not an ape. Adding a little group of letters to a word, such as 'ism', can transform how it interacts with the rest of a sentence. Words can be very specific, or perform different tasks in different circumstances, like 'bow' for example. The same is true for molecules; small changes in structure or context can make a big difference. Some words – war, love, freedom – can change the world. And some molecules have just as much power and influence.

Taking each of fifty-two molecules in turn, this book shows how some individual atoms, when grouped together, take on new and bigger roles. This is not a chemistry text book, however. Instead, the focus is on the tales these compounds have to tell, rather than the chemistry they contain. Choosing fifty-two molecules has been difficult – like choosing just a handful of important words of a language made up of hundreds of thousands. To complicate matters, just as speakers of one language often borrow words from other languages, I have included several combinations of atoms that might be better described as materials, rather than molecules.

Stretching the definition of a molecule beyond its strict scientific limits has allowed me to include minerals that have helped us navigate the globe and polymers that have taken us to the moon. The final fifty-two molecules, compounds and substances range from the fundamental to the frivolous. Some have changed our world, while others simply keep us engaged with life and living. There are the good, the bad and downright smelly. Ultimately, I have included some molecules simply because I find them, or their story, interesting. I hope you do too.

Mole

The cules

Ozone
Location, Location, Location

Ozone is a self-contained love triangle. Like a molecular soap opera, it is the centre of a never-ending cycle of stormy relationships and messy break-ups – the kind of story we love to watch but hate to experience personally. It has taken us a while, but we have learned that these toxic relationships are best kept at a distance.

Atoms usually get together to form molecules for their mutual benefit. Two oxygen atoms happily pair up as O_2, sharing their electrons to satisfy each atom's needs. Occasionally, a third oxygen atom turns up and latches onto O_2. In this newly formed threesome, not everyone gets their fair share of electrons. As far as oxygen is concerned, two is company and three is definitely a crowd.

The break-up of ozone's three-way relationship is inevitable; it just needs the right nudge to cause a split. The oxygen pair return to their original, more sedate state and the third oxygen atom storms off in a huff. What happens then depends on what the newly formed singleton bumps into next. If it finds another lone oxygen, the two pair up immediately to form a happy couple. Or this single oxygen might latch onto another molecule, oxidizing it. That other molecule will be changed by the experience, and not always for the best.

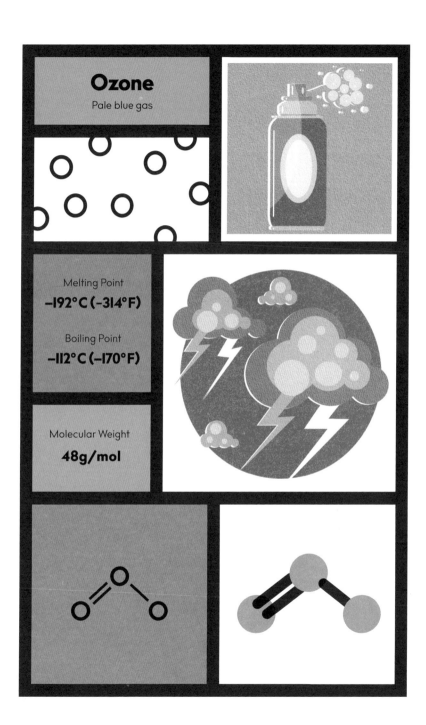

Ozone
Pale blue gas

Melting Point
−192°C (−314°F)

Boiling Point
−112°C (−170°F)

Molecular Weight
48g/mol

Humans had been vaguely aware of ozone's antics for a long time. The ancient Greeks wrote about the sharp smell that occurred around thunderstorms. Scientists conducting electrical experiments in the eighteenth century also noted a distinctive smell around their equipment, but they were not to be distracted from their important work by frivolous sideshows. It was not until the nineteenth century that Christian Friedrich Schönbein isolated the malodorous culprit, a pale blue gas, and named it ozone after the Greek *ozein*, 'to smell'. It was later shown that ozone was O_3, formed when lightning bolts and smaller sparks rip apart and reorganize O_2 molecules.

The Victorians loved being around ozone. They found its dramatic behaviour stimulating. Its fresh, clean, natural smell was certain to be healthy and so they pumped it into hospitals, churches and theatres. These highly strung molecules were enthusiastically sucked into Victorian lungs, but that was where they came undone. Ozone's bit on the side was offloaded onto lung tissue, causing damage. Invigorating could also be irritating. Eventually it was realized that ozone's molecular break-ups were best observed from a distance, ideally several kilometres above Earth's surface.

High above the streets and houses, in a band about 20 km (13 miles) thick and centred between 25 and 35 km (16–22 miles) up, is the ozone layer. The stratosphere is where oxygen atoms go about their assignations and break-ups on a grand scale. At this altitude, ultraviolet light from the sun splits the O_2 molecules it encounters in two. The resulting single oxygen atoms then latch onto other O_2 molecules to make ozone. But these newly formed relationships do not last long. More ultraviolet light, at a different wavelength, breaks up these unstable threesomes. The ongoing saga of getting together and falling apart has been going on for millions of years. The process absorbs much of the sun's harmful ultraviolet radiation, preventing it from damaging organisms living below.

In the twentieth century, a new character was introduced into the drama, in the form of chlorofluorocarbons, or CFCs, used in aerosol cans and as refrigerants, among other things. They appeared to be calm, reliable types that would endure through all manner of chemical trials and tribulations. CFCs became part of the backdrop of our everyday lives, but in the 1980s, they were given a dramatic new story arc. CFC molecules were so stable and unchanging that they hung around for a long time, long enough to make their way up into the upper atmosphere. For the first time they came face to face with intense levels of ultraviolet light, and it tore them apart. Chlorine atoms were liberated from CFCs and went on the rampage, ripping into ozone molecule after ozone molecule. So much ozone was lost from the skies over the Antarctic, that damaging ultraviolet light could reach Earth's surface.

A few plot holes are inevitable in a soap. The hole in the ozone layer above Antarctica appears every spring but, thanks to humans introducing more CFCs, that hole now gapes. Once popular CFCs have become the antagonists. Their role has been restricted but it will take decades to restore balance to the ozone drama.

Sodium Chloride
Salt of the Earth

On 5 May 1930, Mohandas Karamchand Gandhi was arrested and sent to Yerawada Central Jail. His crime was picking up a handful of salt from a beach where the waves had deposited it. Salt, chemically, is a simple thing; Ghandi holding a handful of it aloft was a simple act of defiance; and his imprisonment was a simple response to that defiance. But things are more complex than that.

Salt means different things to different people. To most, it is the white crystalline substance we add to food to preserve or flavour it. To a chemist, that same substance is sodium chloride, just one of many compounds considered to be a salt because it is made up of a balanced combination of oppositely charged atoms. Sodium chloride salt consists of one negatively charged chlorine atom (called chloride) for every positively charged sodium atom. Technically, sodium chloride is not a molecule because, as long as the ratio is one to one, there can be any number of atoms in total in a grain of salt. But salt's role in human and animal life is too great to justify its omission from this book.

To the British Raj in the 1930s, salt was a source of income. It was an appropriate view: 'salt' is the origin of our word salary and the sale of it generated more than 8 per cent of the Raj's revenue. There had been

Sodium Chloride
White crystals

Melting Point
801°C (1474°F)

Boiling Point
1413°C (2575°F)

Molecular Weight
58g/mol

Na⁺ .... Cl⁻

a long-standing government monopoly on the production of salt in India. Though it was abundant, from the sea and from salt flats, it was illegal to collect and refine what nature provided for free. Salt had to be bought from government suppliers, enabling the addition of a heavy tax. The inflated price meant the poorest simply could not afford to buy it and faced jail if they made it for themselves. However, salt is not a luxury item that people can simply forego when money is tight. It is essential for life.

The charged chloride and sodium atoms in salt are easily prized apart by water to float free and act independently. Dissolved in the water of our bodies, chloride goes to make stomach acid and helps cells signal to each other. The sodium enables our nerves to fire and our muscles to move, and it regulates the distribution of water in our cells. Without enough sodium we get headaches, become fatigued, grow nauseous and have difficulty thinking and maintaining our balance. In extreme cases a lack of salt can lead to seizures and coma.

Unlike fat or sugar, we cannot store salt in our bodies long term. The properties that make it so suitable for biological use – high solubility – also mean it is easily lost through sweat and excreta. Fevers and diarrhoea can rapidly reduce salt in the body to dangerously low levels. To ensure we get enough, our body rewards us when we eat salt by telling us it tastes good. And, because plants have no need of sodium, and even meat does not have enough salt to satisfy our daily needs, we must add salt to our food.

  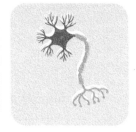

Sodium Chloride

To Gandhi, salt was the perfect symbol of British injustice and provided an opportunity to try out his experiments in mass non-cooperation. He and seventy-eight volunteers set out on a 200-mile (300-km) march to Dandi on the west coast of India. They stopped at every village along the way, gathering followers and making headlines around the world. By the time they reached the ocean, the procession was several thousand strong. Gandhi picked up a handful of salt from the beach and held it aloft as a signal to the rest of India. Millions followed his example of disobeying the salt laws by making their own. More than sixty thousand people were arrested, including Gandhi.

Before his arrest, Gandhi had written to the viceroy announcing his intention of raiding the Dharasana Salt Works with some companions. More than two thousand volunteers went to the site without him. The police ordered them to retreat but they continued towards the salt works unflinching as the police rained down blows on them. Three hundred and twenty were injured, two fatally.

Gandhi was released, unconditionally, on 26 January 1931. His actions, and those of his followers, did not end the salt tax, but it was the start of change. The world was now watching what went on in India. And it was clear that the British could not rule there without the consent of the Indian people.

Water
Taking the Extraordinary for Granted

Humans have long held water in high regard. In ancient times, it was under divine control, the embodiment of deities. It held the elevated status of an element, one of the four fundamental components of all things. Two hundred years ago, science revealed it to be a molecule, a simple combination of hydrogen and oxygen. Its mythical status disappeared overnight, but water never lost its power to impress.

As the sustainer of life and the shaper of worlds, water is a god among molecules. Water saturates our lives. We experience it as solid ice, a flowing liquid and a humid gas. Such behaviour would illicit comment or curiosity in any other substance, yet we accept water's presence on our planet in three different forms as normal, when in fact it is anything but. Water does not behave the way other molecules do. Its components are nothing special and the way they are put together obeys all the chemical rules, but the results are extraordinary.

Water is made up of two hydrogen atoms sitting on an oxygen atom like ears on a teddy bear's head. The oxygen atom is bigger and greedier, hogging the negatively charged electrons that buzz around

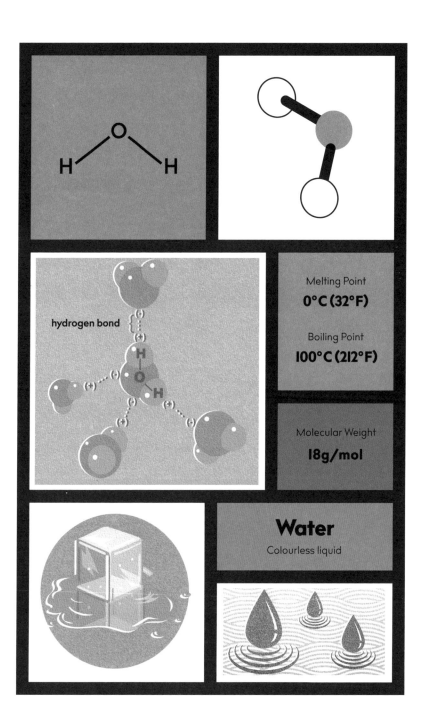

H—O—H

Melting Point
0°C (32°F)

Boiling Point
100°C (212°F)

hydrogen bond

Molecular Weight
18g/mol

Water
Colourless liquid

the molecule and pulling them away from the hydrogen atoms. This unequal sharing makes the oxygen atom slightly negative and the hydrogen atoms slightly positive. A slightly positive hydrogen ear of one water molecule can attract the slightly negative oxygen head of another. Two molecules become linked to each other via a hydrogen bridge. It is these hydrogen bonds that make water, like the gods of Olympus, exceptional.

Without hydrogen bonds to hold onto their neighbours, individual water molecules would head off in all directions, bouncing around any which way as a gas. If water were like other, similar molecules – ammonia (NH_3) and hydrogen sulphide (H_2S), with much weaker bonds between their molecules – Earth would be too warm to be wet. Water's ability to stick together at relatively high temperatures is what gives us clouds, rivers, oceans and life.

All life, as far as we know, needs liquid water. The hydrogen bonds that help water stick together can also latch onto a wide range of other molecules, allowing them to blend seamlessly with each other. Weak attraction to positive and negative regions of other molecules allows water to swarm around and dissolve them. It enables the transport of food, nutrients and waste in and out of the cells of every living thing. This powerful solvent that rains down from the skies has also shifted billions of tonnes of minerals out of rocks and into the seas. Water has shaped us and our landscape in subtle, grandiose and capricious ways that are worthy of an ancient deity.

Many animals and plants rely on fresh water to keep them alive, but water's attraction for salt makes most of it undrinkable. Less than

3 per cent of our world's water is fresh, and less than a tenth of 1 per cent is available to drink. Some is locked away underground. Like the punishment of ancient Greek Tantalus, stuck fast up to his ankles in water that receded out of reach whenever he bent to drink, humans have become more and more thirsty. We drill deeper into ancient aquifers and the water recedes away from us. Most of our fresh water, however, is locked away by those same hydrogen bonds that make liquid water so accessible. It is frozen into ice at the poles.

At room temperature hydrogen bonds clump water molecules together like a packed, bustling crowd. When the temperature drops, there is less energy to move them around. At around 4°C (39°F), there is less jostling and a more formal arrangement is established. The molecules spread out a little. Hydrogen bonds hold the molecules in place, but at arm's length, almost as though respecting personal space. The volume expands, and at 0°C (32°F) the molecules are frozen in place, arranged in the star-like patterns familiar in snowflakes. If water were like other molecules, lakes, ponds and seas would freeze from the bottom up and aquatic life would be very different.

We have learned a lot about what water is over the centuries, but scientists have yet to reach the bottom of all the weird and wonderful ways in which this molecule behaves. Water is still beautiful and mysterious. There may not be mythical beasts lurking in its depths, or gods controlling its flow, but there are still wonders to explore.

Sulphur Dioxide
Food, Glorious Food

Our planet provides a wealth of raw ingredients to keep our appetite sated. Humans have added many more items to the list of edibles through grinding, cooking and other processing techniques. Foods have been combined, seasoned and sweetened into innumerable mouthwatering dishes and beautifully presented to appeal to the eye as well as the stomach. And they have been washed down with liquids that have been steeped, stirred and fermented to bring out new flavours.

Fermentation extends the life of juices and helps kill off bacteria that could make us unwell. We have found many other ways to preserve gluts of food for times of dearth and to kill off pathogens while conserving, even enhancing, flavour. Food can be dried, salted, smoked and pickled. Chemical compounds have been sprinkled and stirred into our food to keep it fresh enough to ship around the world so our tables can be laid with delicacies from every corner of the globe. One of the most tried and tested of these preservatives is sulphur dioxide.

In large quantities, sulphur dioxide is a dense, colourless, toxic, non-flammable gas with the smell of burned matches. It killed thousands of Londoners in December 1952 when unusual weather

Sulphur Dioxide
Colourless gas

Melting Point
−75°C (−99°F)

Boiling Point
−10°C (14°F)

Molecular Weight
64g/mol

conditions trapped sulphur dioxide released from the thousands of coal fires that were common in UK homes at the time. It was the worst 'pea-souper' the city had ever seen and it cloaked the capital for five choking days. Since then, legislation has been passed to clean up the air over our heads, but sulphur dioxide cannot be eliminated completely. Billions of tonnes of it are belched out of volcanoes and other natural, and man-made, sources every year. Nor is it desirable to eradicate it. In small, dilute amounts, sulphur dioxide has none of the toxic effects on humans. We even produce some of our own to keep our heart functioning normally. It also has many benefits for our appetite.

Various things can put us off our food. It can be spoiled by bacteria, yeast and mould. Even the oxygen in the air can react with food to soften biscuits and harden cakes. It bleaches out the pigments in fruit and veg and turns white potatoes and apples brown when they are cut. Sulphur dioxide can help counteract several of these spoilers, as the example of winemaking shows. Fermenting grape juice is a way of extending its shelf-life and, depending on your preference, improving the flavour. The fermentation, turning sugars into alcohol, is done by yeast, but alcohol can also be turned into acetic acid, souring the wine.

Sulphur dioxide diluted down to just one hundred parts in a million is potent enough to kill off bacteria and yeast. The gas can pass through their cell walls and disrupt the activity of important enzymes within. Without knowing the science behind it, Roman vintners knew that burning sulphur candles inside their empty wine vats stopped their wine from turning into vinegar. Though, hopefully, they also knew to

Sulphur Dioxide

leave the room while the disinfection was happening. As the science has become better understood, the use of sulphur dioxide has become more sophisticated, though there is still a considerable art to it.

Crushing grapes exposes the sugary interior to the yeast that grows naturally on the skins, causing them to ferment. But wild yeast does not always give the nicest flavour. Adding the right amount of sulphur dioxide kills off wild yeast so that more desirable, more SO_2-resilient, strains can be added. When the alcohol content is just right, higher levels of sulphur dioxide kill off all the yeast and fermentation ceases.

This additional sulphur dioxide also helps preserve the colour and flavour of the wine in the bottle. The sulphur at the centre of the molecule has space for more than just two oxygen atoms to bond to it. Dissolved in water, a third oxygen atom can be picked up to make sulphite, and a fourth to make sulphate. Sulphites bind to pigment and flavour molecules in place of oxygen. They bleach out brown coloration from white wines, but too much will make red wine appear dull.

Young white wines may retain a whiff of sulphur dioxide but, by the time most wines reach your taste buds, it will have been fully absorbed into the wine. You can safely raise a glass to sulphur dioxide that preserves grapes and many other foods in a form to be savoured.

Silicon Dioxide
Flexible Glass

There once was a Roman craftsman who made an unbreakable glass cup. So pleased was he with his marvellous creation, that he took it as a gift to Emperor Tiberius. The emperor, surrounded by the most beautiful objects in gold, silver and glass, was unimpressed with the simple drinking cup. The craftsman took the cup back and threw it to the floor. To the astonishment of everyone, it bounced.

Picking up the cup, the craftsman showed the emperor it was intact and undamaged save for a tiny dent, which he swiftly made good with a small hammer. The emperor looked at the cup then at the craftsman and beckoned him closer. 'Who else knows how to make glass like this?' he whispered. The craftsman proudly asserted he was the only one; it was his invention. The emperor nodded and dismissed the craftsman, who left the chamber elated, certain that he had won special favour. As soon as the door was closed the emperor called to his chief of staff. 'Have him beheaded!' Fearful that the invention would become more valuable than his own precious possessions, the emperor had the craftsman, his workshop and the secret of flexible glass destroyed.

Glass is a fantastic material: it can be moulded and carved into intricate shapes; it is strong and resistant to chemical attack; it is

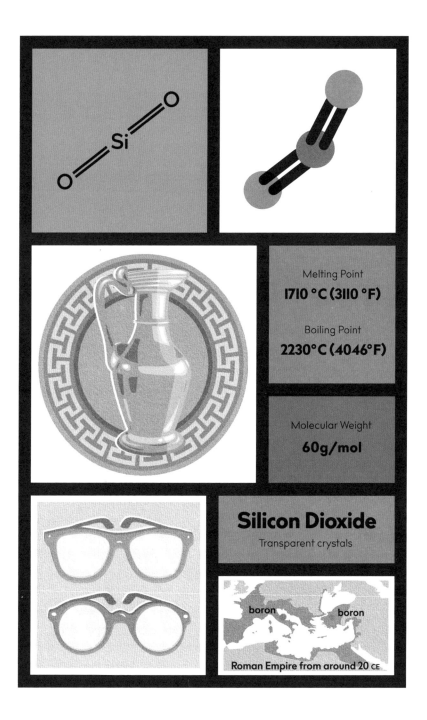

Melting Point
1710 °C (3110 °F)

Boiling Point
2230°C (4046°F)

Molecular Weight
60g/mol

Silicon Dioxide
Transparent crystals

boron   boron

Roman Empire from around 20 CE

transparent and easy to clean. Furthermore, the raw material to make glass, silicon dioxide, or sand, is abundant. For centuries glass has been worked into decorative and practical objects, but chemists, perhaps more than most, have benefited from its remarkable properties. All manner of matter has been manipulated in glass vessels and condensed in glass tubes while allowing scientists to watch the progress of their experiments through transparent walls.

But, for all its strength, resilience and seeming passivity to what goes on around it, glass is easy to shock. A sudden change in temperature or the slightest knock, and it shatters. The atoms of silicon and oxygen that make glass may have the same geometric arrangement as the carbon atoms in diamond, but they are not bonded together with the same strength. This same silicon dioxide is, however, very tolerant of modifications. Of the many metals and minerals that have been added to molten glass to modify its colour, clarity and mouldability, the most common is sodium oxide to make soda-lime glass. The sodium atoms allow the glass to soften at lower temperatures, making it easier to work, but also prone to shattering. Heat causes atoms to vibrate and therefore materials to expand. Sodium atoms vibrate more than the other atoms in glass. Big and sudden changes in temperature make for unequal expansion and the glass breaks.

In the nineteenth century, Otto Schott, Carl Zeiss and Ernst Abbe discovered that adding boric oxide toughened glass, making it resistant to heat and able to withstand the odd knock much better than ordinary glass. It was all down to the boron, atoms of which do not vibrate nearly as much as sodium atoms when heated. This makes borosilicate glass more difficult to work, but safer to use in the oven or when heating a test tube in a laboratory. Many areas of scientific research have been pushed further as a result. Borosilicate glass lenses have been launched into the extreme temperatures of space, with borosilicate glass coatings insulating the shuttles that took them there.

Could a craftsman have found the secret of toughened glass almost two thousand years earlier? The Romans were incredibly sophisticated in their use of glass. Their craftsmanship is evident in the few fragments of glass objects that have survived, but there is no evidence they ever added boron. This is in spite of the fact that there are rich deposits of boron-containing minerals within the bounds of the former Roman Empire. In what is now Turkey, for example, the white boracic mineral pandermite was used locally to make statues and decorative objects. And boric acid was discovered in the exceptionally hot springs in the mountains of Tuscany by Francesco Hoefer, but not until 1777. Perhaps, some time before that, some craftsman found some pretty white crystals there and added them to his molten glass, just to see what would happen. Had the emperor not acted so rashly, would the riches of his empire really have been devalued? Or would his empire have been enriched in other, scientific, ways?

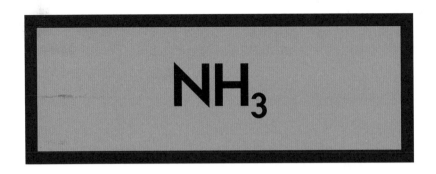

Ammonia
Bread From Air

Ammonia is not glamorous or spectacular. It has no particularly unusual properties or talents. But it is the starting point for so much. Biologically, ammonia is the basis of the amino acids that make up proteins, enzymes and much more besides. Industrially, it can be adapted and manipulated into plastics, pharmaceuticals and fertilizer. There is a lot riding on ammonia. A steady and copious supply of this raw material is a basic requirement to keep everything running. And there is the rub. For something so simple, ammonia is confoundingly difficult to make.

All that is needed to make the three-legged stool that is an ammonia molecule, is to connect four nondescript atoms, three of hydrogen to one of nitrogen. Neither of these elements is in short supply. Hydrogen atoms can be plucked from any number of sources, such as water molecules or the hydrocarbons that are abundant in our environment. Nitrogen is even easier to find. It surrounds us in the very air we breathe. So what is the problem?

The problem is nitrogen. Nitrogen does not go about as a single atom, but pairs up with tight overlapping bonds that are extremely difficult to break. Lightning can separate the atoms by brute force.

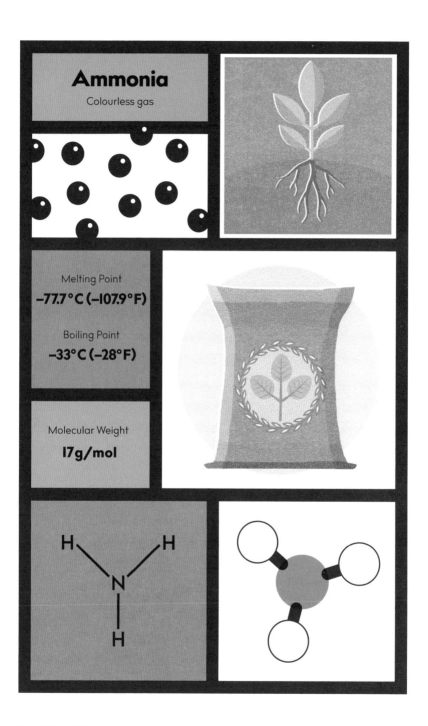

Ammonia
Colourless gas

Melting Point
−77.7°C (−107.9°F)

Boiling Point
−33°C (−28°F)

Molecular Weight
17g/mol

H   H

N

H

And some bacteria can do it through gentle persuasion. A few plants, legumes for example, work with these nitrogen-fixing bacteria, sheltering them in their roots and feeding them carbohydrates in exchange for ammonia. Even though every living thing needs nitrogen compounds to survive, neither these plants, nor any other organism, has worked out how to access the abundance of atmospheric nitrogen for themselves. Perhaps the elaborate arrangement of metals the bacteria have to construct within their nitrogen-fixing enzymes is too difficult. Perhaps it is just easier to let the bacteria and lightning do the work for them.

Therefore, for most of this planet's history, plant and animal growth has been limited by the number of lightning strikes and the efforts of tiny bacteria. It might seem restrictive, but these cottage industries have a phenomenal collective output. Life has hardly been held back at all. But, as humans have multiplied and made their world more complicated, the demand for ammonia has increased.

Just to feed the growing human population, vast amounts of land have been cultivated to grow crops. These crops can pull nitrogen compounds out of the soil faster than bacteria can replace it. Nitrogen-enriching plants can be grown, and fields left fallow to recover, but both limit food production. So, humans developed many ways to recover, recycle and redistribute ammonia from existing nitrogen compounds to try to make up the shortfall. Plants and animal waste, full of nitrogen compounds that have been constructed to keep these organisms alive, are deliberately decomposed to release ammonia.

Ammonia

Nitrogen-rich mineral deposits have been mined, refined and shipped around the world to be dug into the soil.

The biggest nitrogen reserves on the planet remained out of our reach until the twentieth century. Only then did humans learn how to do something single-celled bacteria had been doing for billions of years – take nitrogen from the air and turn it into ammonia. German chemists Fritz Haber and Carl Bosch developed their process in 1909 and it went into industrial production during the First World War, when Germany was cut off from its supply of Chilean nitrates. Unable to match bacteria's sophistication and subtlety, they went for the heavy-handed approach. Their method puts nitrogen under immense pressure and uses metal catalysts to hold its molecules down and force them to open up. Hydrogen atoms are offered, primed and ready for nitrogen to accept them, and the whole lot is heated until it relents. Any nitrogen molecules unwilling to undergo a chemical transformation on the first attempt are cycled around and around until they submit.

Huge factories, carefully integrating one continuous process, pump tonnes of gases through hundreds of metres of pipes, into compressors, over catalysts, through reactors, past coolers and back round again. Despite the difficulties, the scale and number of ammonia factories means there are more molecules of ammonia produced annually than any other industrial chemical. Human ingenuity has given us 'bread from air'. The amount of nitrogen fixed from the atmosphere has been doubled and the output of agricultural land has quadrupled to support more than eight billion humans. But simple, single-celled bacteria, working underground in moderate temperatures and at normal atmospheric pressure, can still make ammonia more easily than us.

Magnetite
Finding Your Way

It was 1754 and the crew of the *Sea Nymph* were hunting whales. They followed the whales further and further north through seas dotted with floating ice. When they reached latitude eighty-two, they found clear sea, but the sailors became increasingly nervous. Their captain wished to push even further north, but the crew refused. The North Pole was a mysterious, unknown place. It could be an ice-free paradise or a land of monsters. There was only one certainty about the north: it was the place that all compasses pointed to. The pole had a power so strong it could turn a needle from as far away as the equator. If they ventured any nearer, the crew feared all the ironwork would be pulled from their ship.

The captain felt he had little choice and ordered a course for home. Certainly, plenty of terrible things might happen if they ventured further north, but he knew his ship sinking through the power of magnets was not one of them. It is true that magnetic materials have a powerful attraction for iron. It is also true that Earth is one very big magnet, but it is not very strong. The tiny magnetic compass needles on board the *Sea Nymph* merely aligned themselves north–south in parallel with the giant magnet beneath them.

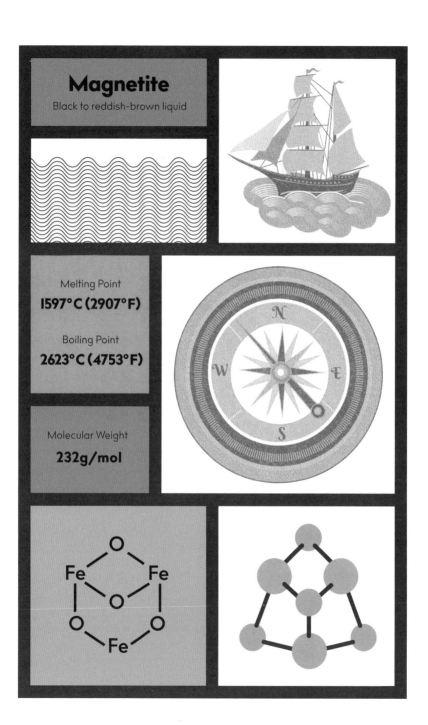

Magnetite
Black to reddish-brown liquid

Melting Point
1597°C (2907°F)

Boiling Point
2623°C (4753°F)

Molecular Weight
232g/mol

All substances have magnetic properties but, for the most part, they go unnoticed in daily life. Every electron within a substance behaves as a tiny magnet, but electrons tend to pair up and their magnetic properties cancel out. Iron is special because its electrons are organized in such a way that several are left unpaired and so the electrons within each atom can be aligned throughout a block of iron, making the whole thing become one magnet. At Earth's core, an enormous lump of iron mixed with another magnetic element, nickel, acts as one giant magnet stretching from one end of the planet to the other.

Humans have been making use of this planet-sized magnet to navigate the globe for at least two thousand years. Centuries earlier, special stones had been discovered that were drawn to each other and to iron. If these stones were suspended, no matter how much they were twisted or turned, they would always align themselves to point in the same direction. Named lodestones ('journey' stones in Middle English), they were naturally magnetized lumps of the mineral magnetite.

Magnetite is a blend of two iron compounds: ferric and ferrous oxide. Each type of iron oxide behaves as a magnet, and they alternate and align in opposite directions, as two bar magnets would do if they were next to each other, but on the molecular scale. This arrangement gives stability but, because the two iron oxides are unevenly matched, one dominates, and the material overall behaves as one magnet. With the exception of extremely rare native iron, magnetite is the most magnetic of all naturally occurring minerals.

Magnetite

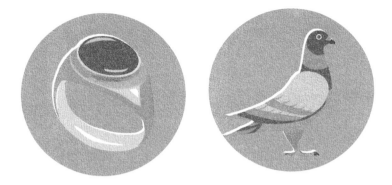

Lodestones were highly prized. Sir Isaac Newton is said to have worn one mounted in his signet ring. In 1661, King Charles II presented the Royal Society, the most prestigious scientific society of the time, with a terrella, a 'little Earth'. This spherical lodestone was used to demonstrate Earth's magnetic field and how a compass needle would align along its north–south axis. Something the sailors on board the *Sea Nymph* clearly had never seen.

Lodestones could be chipped and chiselled into more practical shapes, but melting them and recasting them destroyed their north-finding abilities. However, it was realized that these magnetic abilities could be transferred to needles of iron by hitting them with lodestones. These fine, magnetized needles could then be suspended in air or liquid and used to find north, making navigation much more convenient.

While humans can congratulate themselves on their clever ability to exploit natural phenomena to their advantage, nature has been making use of magnetite for much longer than us. Magnetotactic bacteria draw in iron from their environment and work it into tiny, high-quality crystals of magnetite that pull them into alignment with Earth's magnetic field. Homing pigeons have magnetite in their beaks, though how, and if, it helps them navigate by magnetic fields is still a mystery. Tiny magnetite crystals have been found in many other animals, including humans, though their role is much debated. It is possible that magnetite may have helped many creatures explore their world and find their way home again.

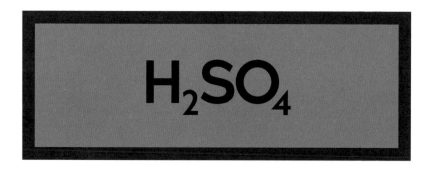

Sulphuric Acid
The Status Symbol

Nations like to know how they measure up to others. It can be for all sorts of reasons: trade, war or reputation. And various indicators have been used to find out where a country sits in the global rankings such as its wealth, the size of its lands, the happiness of its people or its contributions to science and the arts. One little molecule, and how much of it a country produces, has also been used as a measure of industrial and economic strength.

Pedanius Dioscorides was a first-century Greek physician and botanist whose work, *De materia medica*, influenced medicine into the sixteenth century. Around the same time, Gaius Plinius Secundus, known as Pliny the Elder, wrote his *Naturalis Historia*, which became the model for encyclopedias. Both wrote about medical treatments and herbs, and both were citizens of the Roman Empire, which, at the time, encompassed the entire Mediterranean region and much beyond it. What have the Romans ever done for us? Well, they made the first documented references to vitriol, the starting point of sulphuric acid.

Eight hundred years later, another civilization was blossoming in Persia. Islamic scholars were making great advances in astronomy, mathematics and chemistry. Around 900 CE, Abū Bakr Muhammad

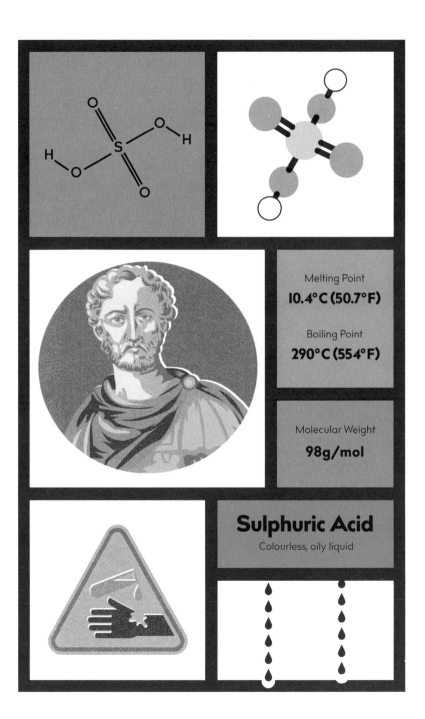

Melting Point
10.4°C (50.7°F)

Boiling Point
290°C (554°F)

Molecular Weight
98g/mol

Sulphuric Acid
Colourless, oily liquid

ibn Zakariyyā al-Rāzī, physician, philosopher and alchemist, published his *Book of Secrets*, in which he classified all substances known to him. He was the first to systematically categorize substances based on their properties. He used four headings: animal, vegetable, mineral and derivatives of the first three. In his table of minerals, he included a subdivision of six similar glassy compounds that could be identified individually by their colour. We now know al-Rāzī had correctly grouped together metal sulphates, blue copper and green iron ones, along with a misplaced alum compound.

Medieval Europeans gave these sulphate compounds the name vitriol from the Latin *vitrum*, meaning 'glass'. The intensity of these blue and green compounds could vary with the amount of water trapped within their crystal structure. And they noted the water, *phlegma vitrioli*, could be sweated out of them when heated. At higher temperatures the vitriol would break down further to release its 'spirit', or sulphur dioxide, that, if left to stand, would combine with water and oxygen from the air, to make 'oil of vitriol', or sulphuric acid. Oil of vitriol was a formidable and useful solvent that could eat its way through most metals and burn through cloth and paper. But its full potential would not be realized until the Industrial Revolution.

Britain is a nation known for many things, including the export of methods and principles of mass manufacturing. The iron that was used to build the structures, machines and tools that facilitated this

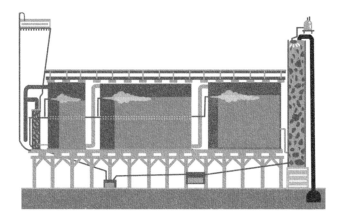

Sulphuric Acid

large-scale mechanization relied on sulphuric acid for its production. As did the paper, cloth and chemical industries, as well as a whole host of others that were burgeoning in the eighteenth century.

In the seventeenth century, Johann Rudolf Glauber, Bavarian-born but resident in various parts of Europe, devised a method of making sulphuric acid in bulk to meet the increasing demand. He is credited as the first industrial chemist. His method involved burning sulphur in the presence of saltpetre and steam. Production was scaled up by Joshua Ward, a British pharmacist, and adapted by another Brit, John Roebuck, into the 'lead chamber process' that remained the industry standard for the next two centuries. The acid it produced was strong, but at 65 per cent, later refined up to 78 per cent, it was not always strong enough. The really strong stuff was still made by roasting iron sulphate, the medieval alchemical way, up until the nineteenth century.

Then, in 1831, British vinegar merchant Peregrine Phillips devised the contact process. In this method, a metal catalyst was used to persuade sulphur dioxide to take on an extra oxygen atom. The resulting sulphur trioxide was then added to sulphuric acid to make oleum, or fuming sulphuric acid. Oleum could be diluted in water to make any strength sulphuric acid that might be required. It is how most sulphuric acid is manufactured today, and in staggering quantities.

At around 180 million tonnes per year, sulphuric acid is the world's most widely used industrial chemical. Almost every manufactured item comes into contact with it at some stage. In recent years, its main use has been in manufacturing phosphate fertilizers. Sulphuric acid started as a chemical curiosity, became an industrial yardstick, and is now an indicator of agricultural activity.

LiFePO$_4$

Lithium Iron Phosphate
The Spark of Life

Physicist and chemist Alessandro Volta changed the world, and all to settle an argument over a dead frog. It started with Luigi Galvani, an anatomist who was interested in the effect of electricity on muscles. He passed sparks from a static electricity machine along the nerves in frogs' legs to make the muscles contract. After hundreds of experiments, and even more frogs, he realized he did not need the static electricity machine. The frogs' legs could be made to move simply by bridging the nerve and muscle with a curved strip of metal. He published his theory of an animal electricity that animated all creatures and could be released to flow through metal to make a frog's legs twitch. Volta thought this was nonsense.

An epistolary argument raged between the two scientists for years. Volta maintained it was the metal that was the source of the electricity and Galvani was adamant it was the frog. To prove his point, Volta invented a device using just metals, and no frog, to generate electricity. He stacked up alternating discs of silver and zinc sandwiched between pieces of pasteboard soaked in salt water to represent the frog. Wires connected to the top and bottom of his pile could be touched together to produce a spark, or applied to a dead frog to make the nerves twitch.

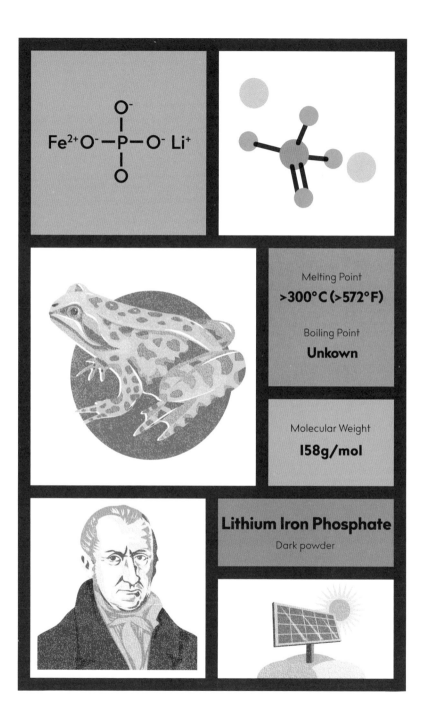

Fe^{2+} O$^-$ —P—O$^-$ Li$^+$

Melting Point
>300°C (>572°F)

Boiling Point
Unkown

Molecular Weight
158g/mol

Lithium Iron Phosphate
Dark powder

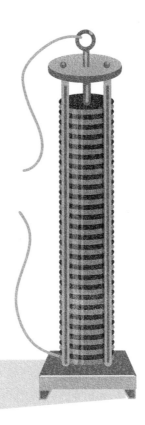

Volta's pile of metals and pasteboard was a reliable, portable power source. It was easy to make, and its output could be varied in predictable, stepwise fashion by changing the number of pairs of discs and how they were arranged. Rows of columns could be wired together to make powerful batteries. Within weeks of a description of the pile appearing in the press, William Nicholson and Anthony Carlisle had built their own version and used it to prise apart water. Their experiment confirmed that water was not an element in its own right, but made of oxygen and hydrogen. Ever more powerful batteries were built and used to pull apart compounds that had resisted the heat of furnaces and corrosive chemical attack. Electricity revealed their true composition and isolated previously unknown elements. In 1821, William Thomas Brande used a voltaic pile to isolate lithium for the first time, a metal that would become very important in future battery technology.

Most batteries need two different metals, and the more different the better. One way to distinguish between metals is their reactivity. A reactive metal wants to lose its negative electrons more than a less reactive metal. Pairing a reactive metal with a less reactive metal means negatively charged electrons flow from one to the other, and moving positive and negative charges is what electricity is all about.

Lithium's high reactivity makes it an excellent choice to get charges moving, but it often reacts with things you do not want it to, like water and oxygen. It is far too reactive to use as a pure metal, but there are other ways to manage it safely. Remove a negatively charged electron from a lithium atom and it becomes a much less reactive positively charged lithium ion. Get the positively charged lithium ions to move, and you have a battery.

Lithium iron phosphate is just one of many chemical combinations that have been developed to keep lithium ions safely contained but still able to move. This naturally occurring mineral has lithium ions threaded through an iron and phosphate framework. Applying a current pulls the positive lithium out of the framework towards the negative end of the battery. Allowing them to flow back into the framework creates a current that powers our devices. The lithium ions can be shunted back and forth thousands of times, making it rechargeable. Excess electrical energy can be effectively stored until it is needed and, without wires connecting us to the mains supply, we are free to take that power with us wherever we go.

Electricity, with the help of Volta's pile, facilitated the modern world. Nowadays, changes in the world are influencing our use of batteries. As more energy is generated from solar and wind power, we will become increasingly reliant on batteries to store that energy to use when the sun is not shining and the breeze drops. The basic principles behind batteries have not changed in the two hundred years since Volta's invention. Another radical scientific breakthrough may be needed to power our future.

Carbon Dioxide
Smoke and Bubbles

Jan Baptist van Helmont was a seventeenth-century intellectual gadfly. He flitted between medicine, philosophy and chemistry, asking awkward questions and noticing things a lot of other people seemed to have missed. Today, he is remembered for three things: the invention of the word 'gas', his willow tree experiment and the discovery of carbon dioxide. What he did not realize was that they were all connected.

In his willow tree study, Helmont applied a precision and dedication to measurement that was rare in experimenters of his day. He carefully weighed the tree, the soil and the pot at the start of his experiment and then for the next five years added only water. While the weight of the pot and the soil did not change, the tree got bigger. Naturally enough, Helmont assumed the water was being transformed into making more tree. He was, at least, partly right.

Helmont conducted many other experiments. In one, he watched chalk diminish as he dropped acid onto it. The acid was causing something to escape from the chalk, but what? In another experiment he burned charcoal inside a closed vessel and discovered the remaining ash weighed less than the original charcoal, but he could not see anything else in the vessel. The charcoal appeared to have simply

Carbon Dioxide

Carbon Dioxide

Colourless gas

Sublimation Point
**−78.48°C
(−109.26°F)**

Molecular Weight
44g/mol

vanished into thin air. Obviously, Helmont was not the first person to watch combustible material go up in smoke, or watch chalk fizz in contact with acids, but he was perhaps the first to realize that there was more to it than just smoke and bubbles.

Before Helmont appeared on the scene, the world had got along perfectly fine with words like 'smoke', 'vapour', 'mist' and 'air'. There were different varieties of all of these, of course. There were good airs and bad airs and ordinary, everyday airs. But Helmont was not satisfied with this. So, he took the Greek word *chaos* and manipulated it into 'gas' to describe 'a far more subtle or fine thing than a vapour, mist or distilled oiliness, although as yet it be many times thicker than air.' The gas from his charcoal and chalk experiments he named *gas sylvestris*, or wild gas, because he was unable to condense it in the way that steam can be condensed into water, or smoke deposits soot. He realized, too, that this gas was the same gas given off during fermentation and that made the air in some caves and mines unbreathable.

Gas sylvestris had been around long before Helmont stumbled upon it. In fact, long before any humans were around to ignore it. It is believed to have made up a large proportion of the first atmosphere that formed around this planet. Over millions of years, it combined with rocks, was washed out of the sky by rain and absorbed by plants to be replaced by oxygen. Around ten thousand years ago, levels of this gas in the air settled to around 280 parts in every million. It is not surprising such a small amount was overlooked. Despite Helmont's revelations, the gas continued to be ignored until Joseph Black rediscovered it around 1750.

Carbon Dioxide

Black heated some limestone and found it gave off a variety of air he had not come across before. It was not from bubbles trapped inside the rock, but the rock itself changing into something else. He named this new air 'fixed air', because the separated air and rock could also be reunited. The heated rock could be dissolved in water, to make limewater, and the air it had released could be bubbled through it, turning the water cloudy as the air became 'fixed' into limestone again.

Eventually *gas sylvestris*, or fixed air, got its proper name, carbon dioxide. It was shown that it was the carbon dioxide combining with water using photosynthesis that gave Helmont's willow tree its added bulk. And now that we know about carbon dioxide, we have found many uses for it – from fizzy drinks and fire extinguishers, to lasers and decaffeinating coffee.

The volume of combustibles burned has dramatically increased since Helmont's day. Since Black's day, limestone has been heated to produce cement to such a degree that concrete has become the world's most consumed material after water. All of these activities contribute to ever-increasing amounts of carbon dioxide in our atmosphere, which traps ever-increasing amounts of heat on our planet. After spending so much time in obscurity, we can no longer ignore carbon dioxide's presence.

CH$_4$N$_2$O

Urea
Another Man's Waste

How do you solve a problem like urea? It is a socially awkward thing, an irritant that shows up at inconvenient moments as an uncomfortable presence asking difficult questions. There is no shortage of it in our lives, but its presence is not always welcome, chemically, biologically or socially. But one organism's waste is often another organism's riches. Urea, whether it is perceived as good or bad, is just urea. And, for nineteenth-century chemists, that was also a problem.

Until the eighteenth century, urea was incognito. Roughly 25g (1oz) of it was being produced every day by every adult human, but was flushed away unnoticed along with all the other waste products they, and other animals, produced. Then along came Dutch scientist Herman Boerhaave. Boerhaave thought of the human body as a beautiful and intricate biological machine of pipes, pumps and levers. He carried out systematic and extensive examinations to try to unpick the details of this living mechanism. In 1727, he reported the discovery of a pure chemical from human urine, a solid he called 'the native salt of urine', presumably because it formed colourless crystals. It was a strong hint that the mysterious life processes going on within our bodies were chemical in nature.

Melting Point
135°C (275°F)

Boiling Point
Breaks down

Molecular Weight
60g/mol

Urea
White crystals

As the eighteenth century progressed, so did scientific theories and techniques that could be used to produce evidence supporting or contradicting those theories. New methods were developed to isolate and investigate urea, as it became known. It was also found to be present in the urine of a wide variety of animals. Nature appeared to be using the same basic chemistry, but that chemistry, and the compounds it created, seemed to be very different to those that scientists could produce in their laboratories. The theory of vitalism was invoked to rationalize these differences.

One aspect of vitalism divided all chemical compounds into two broad categories: inorganic and organic. Substances made in a laboratory were inorganic. They might change when heated, but they could be recovered again. Organic substances, like urea, were produced by nature using some unknown vital ingredient. Organic compounds had a tendency to transform into something else when heated and could not be recovered. The explanation was that organic compounds retained part of the essential life force that created them, but this vital component was driven off by heat. The search for more organic compounds, and the vital force, spark or substance that made them, became the focus of a lot of scientific attention.

Then, in 1828, German chemist Friedrich Wöhler carried out an experiment that produced urea from inorganic compounds, 'without thereby needing to have kidneys, or anyhow, an animal, be it human or dog.' This laboratory-made urea was indistinguishable from animal-made urea. A crack had appeared in the theory of vitalism and Wöhler had initiated a new branch of chemistry: organic chemistry. It was a

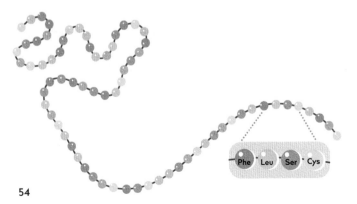

Phe Leu Ser Cys

Urea

Cys

defining moment in chemical science. Ever more compounds were isolated from natural sources and later reproduced in exact detail by scientists in their laboratories. The theory of vitalism crumbled and organic chemistry expanded to become the study of any chemical, be it natural or synthetic, that contained carbon atoms.

Urea is an organic compound in every sense of the word. Every molecule contains a central carbon atom connected to an oxygen, as well as two symmetrical amine groups. Amines are composed of a nitrogen and two hydrogen atoms, the chemical group that gives amino acids half of their name, and a clue to the source of urea in nature. Amino acids make up the proteins and enzymes that make biological processes possible. Every organism needs its own bespoke set of proteins and enzymes to cater to its specific needs. The protein we eat is broken up into its constituent amino acids, which are then restrung into new proteins using instructions from an individual's DNA. Breaking up proteins produces ammonia, a compound far too toxic for our bodies to tolerate in the quantities we make daily. So, it is converted into far less toxic urea, before it is excreted. But this waste is not wasted. Urea is easily converted back into ammonia that plants can take up and use to build their own amino acids and proteins.

Humans encourage plant growth using urea produced by animals and in factories. In excess, plant growth can crowd out and choke other species. Properly managed, urea can help feed our huge human population. Whether it is causing or solving problems, produced artificially or biologically, urea is always just urea.

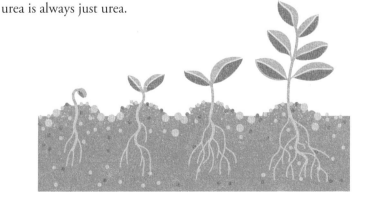

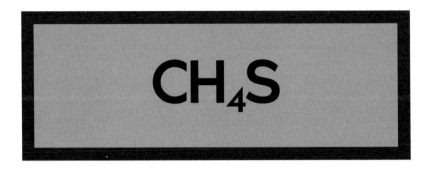

Methanethiol
The Big Stink

One summer's day, not so long ago, the residents of the English town of Waltham Abbey were assaulted by the most fearful stink. The streets, shops and homes in this picturesque market town were filled with not just a bad smell, but a stench so overwhelmingly awful some sought hospital treatment convinced they were being poisoned. Others rang the local gas supplier fearful a broken gas main could blow their small town to kingdom come. This alarming situation was all caused by a minor leak of a tiny molecule called methanethiol.

The ability of this obnoxious little compound to cause offence is out of all proportion to its size or propensity to do harm. Methanethiol is composed of just six atoms that together can clear a room long before an occupant is likely to have inhaled a dangerous dose. This molecule's insufferable behaviour is almost entirely down to just one of its six atoms – sulphur. Without sulphur, methanethiol would just be odourless methane, or natural gas, a single carbon atom surrounded by four hydrogens. A sulphur atom, wedged between the carbon and one of the hydrogens, changes everything. The arrangement of carbon-sulphur-hydrogen is the defining chemical feature of a particularly pungent family of molecules called mercaptans.

Methanethiol

Colourless liquid

Melting Point
−123°C (−189.4°F)

Boiling Point
5.94°C (42.7°F)

Molecular Weight
48g/mol

Sulphur compounds are notoriously stinky. Anything that smells bad in biology is probably down to some sulphur-containing molecule somewhere because the element is integral to life. Sulphur-containing molecules, such as the amino acids methionine and cysteine, are part of the chemical machinery that keeps life moving. To ensure we and everything else stays healthy, sulphur compounds must be constantly fed into the food chain. And what goes in can also come out.

Some single-celled organisms can break down methionine and cysteine into simpler sulphur-containing compounds that are light enough to escape the organism. Drifting through the air and into our noses, these odorous compounds act as signals. The powerful smell of dimethyl sulphide released by marine algae is one of the main contributors to the smell of the sea. Sea birds can follow its scent to find high concentrations of algae where there are also likely to be lots of fish feeding on it.

More often, these small sulphur-containing molecules act as a warning. For example, 3-methyl-2-butene-1-thiol is another member of the mercaptan family and the key compound in the skunk's smelly defence. But, however much your senses try to convince you otherwise, the compound is not particularly toxic. Its bark is far worse than its bite, but still a very effective way of establishing personal boundaries. Skunks concentrate this compound in their spray to ensure their signals are received loud and clear. Not all chemical cues are so blunt.

Methanethiol

Decomposition is a natural part of life, but for many organisms it is something to be avoided. The bacteria involved in decay can cause sickness and death, but they are too small to be seen and so we have evolved other ways to detect their presence. Our brains are programmed to revolt when the sulphurous by-products of bacterial feasting are detected. The smell of rotten eggs, decaying cabbage, bad breath and smelly feet disgusts us because we are smelling microbial-made methanethiol. Humans can detect the presence of just one methanethiol molecule diluted among a billion others. It is so effective at compelling us to move away from the smell that methanthiol and related compounds are added to odourless natural gas to warn of leaks. This very effective chemical alarm has kept us safe from food poisoning and the build-up of highly flammable gas. Which brings us back to Waltham Abbey and the big stink.

In the summer of 1992, methanethiol escaped from the Pan Britannica Industries plant close to Waltham Abbey town. It was one of the compounds being used to make the insecticide dimethoate. There must have been quite a lot of it on site and in a concentrated form, but even a small leak diluted on a summer breeze would produce an unholy stench. Those that felt unwell were reacting as their body had been primed to do, to overreact and get away from something that might not be good for them. Those that phoned the gas company were responding to the familiar warning smell. Thankfully, on this occasion, the chemical alarm was a false one.

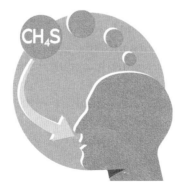

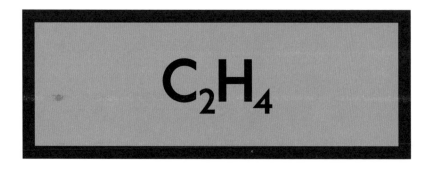

Ethene
The Ripe Banana

Have you ever woken up and wondered what day it is? If you have, spare a thought for the nineteenth-century city-dwellers across Europe and America who woke up wondering what month it was. The tree-lined boulevards of Lille, Berlin and New York were showing their autumn colours. Leaves were yellowing and dropping to the pavements . . . but it was the height of summer. The introduction of street lighting at the start of the century had already changed the pattern of day and night, and now it was messing around with the seasons.

The revolution in illumination was brought about by the discovery of fuel gas. When coal, oil and wood are heated in an atmosphere of reduced oxygen, they release gases that burn particularly brightly. These gases were piped along city streets and into lamps to lengthen the days in London, Paris, Berlin and beyond. And where the lamps and the lights appeared, the trees started to do strange things. Some would show a sudden growth spurt, while others withered and died. One street would be full of green leaves and the next would show the bare branches of winter. The trees seemed to have lost all track of time.

Many theories were put forward to explain the strange behaviour. Perhaps hard, compacted earth was covering the roots and restricting

H-C=C-H (with H above and below each C)

Melting Point
–169.1°C (–272.4°F)

Boiling Point
–103.7°C (–154.7°F)

Molecular Weight
28g/mol

Ethene
Colourless gas

access to water and oxygen? Could an insect pest or fungal disease be responsible? Was it down to unseasonably high temperatures or low rainfall? There were many factors to take into consideration, until a few big leaks of illuminating gas and the subsequent death of nearby trees raised suspicions of the real cause.

Leaky gas pipes were common enough, but not all trees and streets were affected and not all in the same way. So, experiments were conducted. Coal gas was pumped past tree roots and the leaves watched closely for any change. The results were inconclusive, but this was not all that unexpected. Trees are complicated things, and so was illuminating gas. It could contain carbon dioxide, carbon monoxide, nitrogen, hydrogen, methane, napthalene, ethene and plenty else. Both the component compounds and their proportions varied depending not just on whether coal, oil or wood was heated to produce it, but also on the manufacturer and whether the fuel was purified before being pumped into the pipes.

It was not until the turn of the twentieth century that ethene was finally revealed to be the cause of the trees' seasonal disruption. It was a surprise. There were far more toxic compounds to be found in illuminating gas, but it was the tiny proportion of ethene that was causing such startling effects. Ethene, a simple molecule of two carbon and four hydrogen atoms shaped like a bowtie, turned out to be an important plant hormone. Plants and trees made ethene within their own cells, the levels waxing and waning throughout a plant's life, influencing the rhythms of everything from seed germination to

ageing, and root growth to leaf loss. Extra ethene from leaky gas pipes was causing all sorts of confusion.

The realization then came that humans had been using ethene to manipulate plants for thousands of years without knowing it. The ancient Egyptians scored figs to help them ripen. The Chinese burned incense in closed rooms to ripen pears. Producing ethene is part of a plant's natural response to damage and environmental stresses, as well as the chemical that ripens their fruit.

As illuminating gas fell out of favour and was replaced by more reliable and safer lighting, city trees returned to their usual timetable. But ethene is still shifting the seasons. Released into fields, orchards and olive groves, it ensures that pineapples blossom, melons reach maturation and olives are easier to harvest, and all at the same time. Bananas are picked green and packaged in sealed containers with sachets of silica gel loaded with potassium permanganate to soak up stray ethene molecules, before being shipped all over the world. Upon arrival in cooler climes, a whiff of ethene ripens them off before they hit supermarket shelves. Flowers that are cut and transported many thousands of miles arrive fresh because they are wrapped in ethene-absorbing materials. So, now, it is our supermarket shelves that throw off our sense of time with fruit and vegetables available year-round and delivered to us in excellent condition, and all thanks, in part, to ethene.

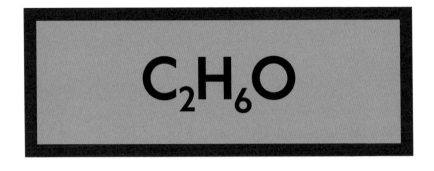

$$C_2H_6O$$

Ethanol
A Drink to Lily the Pink

To a chemist, alcohol is a specific name for a lot of compounds. To everyone else, it is one compound with a lot of names – booze, sauce, hooch, the hard stuff, mother's ruin. It is a social lubricant and a catalyst for creativity, poor decisions, recklessness, accidents and violence. This is a lot to take on for one molecule. Such huge social responsibilities would be enough to drive anyone to drink, and alcohol certainly behaves as if it has had a few too many.

The key compound that puts the demon in the drink is ethanol, the second smallest molecule in the family of alcohols. This family is characterized chemically by having an oxygen and hydrogen (-OH) group attached to a chain of carbon atoms. Ethanol has only two carbons in its chain, and five hydrogens attached to them, but it makes the body of the molecule greasy enough to be absorbed into fats and oils. By contrast, the -OH head of ethanol loves water. The molecule is therefore equally at home in fatty and watery environments and, together with its tiny size, this means ethanol can squeeze into almost every bodily nook and cranny.

An ethanol molecule looks like a miniature balloon dog and it bounces around inside the body like a drunkard. It bumps into things

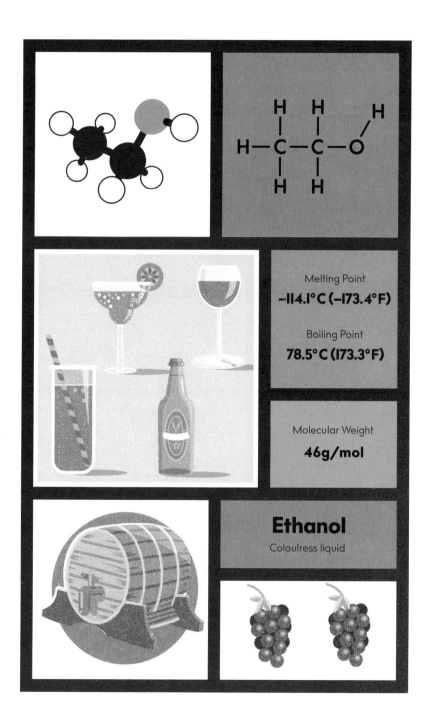

Melting Point
−114.1°C (−173.4°F)

Boiling Point
78.5°C (173.3°F)

Molecular Weight
46g/mol

Ethanol
Coloulress liquid

and gets stuck in awkward places, including a wide range of receptors. These receptors are the biological docking points for the molecular instructions that keep our bodies functioning. Ethanol may not be such a good fit as the usual chemical messenger, but it can cause enough disruption and distortion to change the tone of the message, making it louder, quieter or garbled.

Inside the brain, alcohol can moderately increase the amount of dopamine, the feel-good signal, released from cells. It can simultaneously dial down the effects of other chemicals that excite nerves, such as glutamate. The result can be relaxing, but it can also slow our thinking, slur our speech and make our movements uncoordinated. Throughout the body are receptors that are sensitive to pressure, temperature and chemical stimulation that alert us to possible danger. Alcohol can fool the temperature sensors into raising the alarm, putting the fire in firewater and giving the illusion of a warming dram.

Scientists have been left struggling to unpick the huge number of interactions, complications and knock-on effects ethanol can induce. To add to the confusion, the consequences and impact of ethanol's many interactions vary enormously. Some, like the sensation of burning, do not translate into actual damage. Others, like metabolism of alcohol in the liver, can destroy cells. What everyone does agree on is that a lot of alcohol has serious consequences for health that can even lead to death. In moderation, however, some of these effects can be good – though what quantifies moderation and if the good outweighs the bad is still debated. It is not surprising that attitudes to alcohol can veer wildly from glass half empty to glass half full. The ancient Romans held it in high esteem, referring to it as *aqua vitae* or the 'water of life' because of its positive and stimulating attributes. In times and places where water was not always potable, beer, and other weak alcoholic drinks, were healthier alternatives.

Alcohol has long been a part of medicine. Ethanol can aid the extraction of active compounds from other herbal remedies used in the past and can enhance the effects of other drugs, such as the morphine in opium. But this could be as dangerous as it might be beneficial. Sometimes alcohol was the medicine itself. Even temperance societies were not against the use of alcohol for medicinal purposes, offering respite from illness and America's periodic prohibition laws.

The popularity of Lydia Pinkham's Vegetable Compound was not due, perhaps, to its mix of five herbs, but the 20 per cent alcohol they were dissolved in. Launched in 1873, it was marketed at housewives who were encouraged to 'Trust Lydia Pinkham, not the doctor who doesn't understand your problems.' It inspired several ribald drinking songs and made Mrs Pinkham very rich. Used in the recommended medicinal doses, the alcohol may even have been of benefit.

Some studies have shown low doses of alcohol can ward off the common cold and heart disease, though exactly how is unclear. The results and the recommended dose are also disputed. Ethanol's drunken bumbling through the body might do some accidental good.

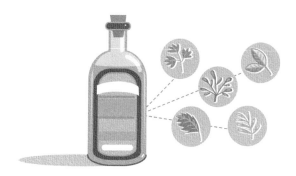

$$(C_2F_4)_n$$

Polytetrafluoroethene
The Teflon Coat

In 1951, Alec Guinness was chased down a street by an angry mob. His character, Sidney Stratton, had invented a material that would not stain and never wore out. One set of clothes would last a lifetime. Mill owners and workers, fearing ruin, tried to stop him. *The Man in the White Suit* was science fiction but, unbeknown to the filmmakers, it was not so far from science fact.

A tough synthetic material, with such low surface friction that almost nothing stuck to it, had been available since 1938. Unlike Stratton's fictional fibre, this material was made by accident in the DuPont laboratories. American chemist Roy Plunkett was investigating CFCs, gases used as refrigerants. He was using cylinders of the gas tetrafluorethene in his experiments, but one cylinder stopped releasing gas before it was empty. Intrigued as to what was going on, Plunkett cut the cylinder open. Inside he found a white, waxy powder with a curiously slippery feel.

Plunkett quickly realized he had a new polymer on his hands. The iron cylinder had acted as a catalyst, opening one of the two bonds between the carbon atoms in the tetrafluorethene molecules and allowing them to link together. It was like cutting open paper rings and

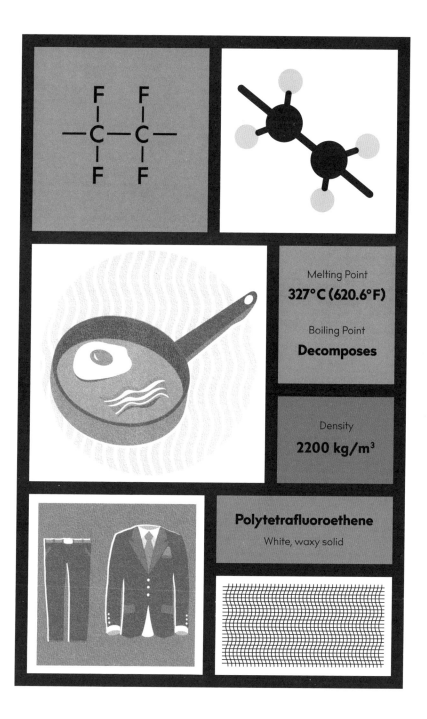

Melting Point
327°C (620.6°F)

Boiling Point
Decomposes

Density
2200 kg/m³

Polytetrafluoroethene
White, waxy solid

The Teflon Coat

joining the ends together into a long chain, but with around 50,000 tetrafluoroethene molecules strung into one polytetrafluoroethene (PTFE) chain. The fibre of the film was a complex mix of ingredients. By comparison, PTFE was simplicity itself, just two elements: a long chain of carbon atoms almost completely covered by a sheath of fluorine atoms. This simple arrangement gave the material some unusual properties.

The bonds within the polymer, between the carbon atoms along the backbone and the carbon–fluorine bonds along its length, are difficult to break, giving PTFE strength and resilience. The fluorine atoms that form the outward face of the polymer maintain a tight hold on their electrons. The result is a uniform indifference to other atoms that want to interact with them. Water and oil run off PTFE's back. Boiling acids and caustic compounds are shrugged off as if they were nothing. The slim polymer chains, with few side branches, pack together particularly efficiently, helping maintain the polymer's performance in extreme cold and at high temperatures. DuPont christened the new polymer Teflon and looked for ways to use it. It was perfect for the advanced science of the Manhattan Project, protecting the pipework and seals from the corrosive effects of the uranium hexafluoride passing through them to be refined into the atom bomb. It remained a specialist material for niche applications until 1954, when Teflon was domesticated.

Polytetrafluoroethene

French engineer Marc Grégoire, tired of tangles, decided to coat his fishing tackle with PTFE. His wife Colette, tired of scouring saucepans, urged him to apply the same nonstick coating to a frying pan. But how do you stick a nonstick substance? By etching the metal surface of a saucepan and allowing liquid polymer to flow into the cracks and crevices. When it cooled and hardened into one smooth sheet, it was trapped. Teflon-coated pans were tough enough to resist the heat of cooking, slippery enough to stop food sticking, and its chemical indifference meant it did not taint the food. Consumers loved it. PTFE has since been applied to many different surfaces from skis to space shuttles, and cables to catheters. But, in the growing list of things that benefited from PTFE, there was a notable absence.

Despite DuPont's interests in fibre and fabrics, PTFE was not woven into a Sydney Stratton-style white suit. The same properties that made it so appealing also made it uncomfortable to wear. PTFE repelled stains on the outside, but it also repelled sweat on the inside, trapping it against the body. The Teflon coat worn by many politicians would remain metaphorical until 1969. Bob Gore was slowly stretching heated rods of PTFE when, tired of waiting, he yanked at the polymer. It immediately stretched to eight times its length and microscopic pores appeared within it. These pores were too small to allow droplets of water through but big enough for water vapour to escape. Waterproof but breathable, stain-resistant and hard-wearing, expanded PTFE, layered with other materials, became Gore-Tex. Fortunately for Gore, he is unlikely to suffer the same consequences as Sydney Stratton. PTFE is not indestructible and changing fashion will keep manufacturers in business.

C_3H_6OS

Propanethial-S-Oxide
The Booby Trap

There are many myths and legends surrounding *Allium cepa*. Some say it can heal wounds, others that it can ward off evil. It is not exactly a golden idol in a remote South American cave, or the Ark of the Covenant, but it is protected by booby traps nonetheless. Thankfully, you do not have to be Indiana Jones to get to *cepa*'s treasure. Millions of us set off these traps every day, and suffer the consequences, for the rewards that lie within.

Allium cepa is the humble onion. It is a common enough plant, but its juice has been held to have some miraculous properties. For centuries, skin has been smeared with onion to heal wounds and prevent scaring, though more recent scientific studies have failed to show any benefits. Other claims of onions preventing bone density loss have shown promise. However, no one would be able to eat the quantity of onions needed for medical benefit, and if they did it would doubtless cause other problems. Other applications have proved more successful. Onion oil is used to ward off carrot flies, though claims of success against evil spirits are more difficult to substantiate. The onion's main application is, of course, in food. Nutritionally, it is little to write home about, but it is packed full of flavour. The true value of onions

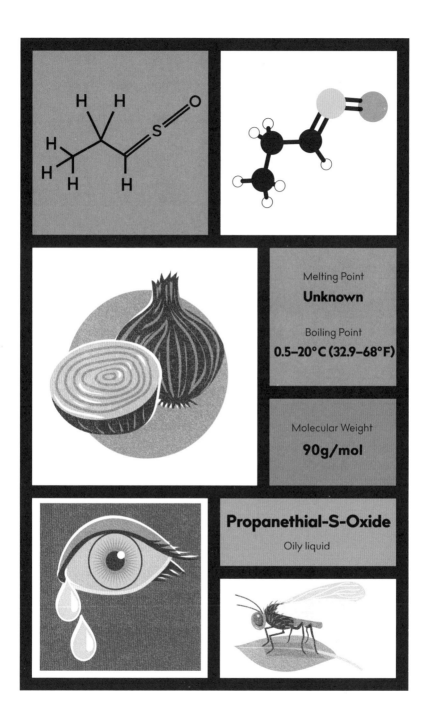

Melting Point
Unknown

Boiling Point
0.5–20°C (32.9–68°F)

Molecular Weight
90g/mol

Propanethial-S-Oxide
Oily liquid

lies in the number of dishes they have enhanced around the world and for thousands of years. But those tasty treats are protected.

Plenty of plants protect themselves from being munched and use a variety of vicious tricks: thorns; tough bark or shells to protect seeds; irritating, bitter or toxic sap. Some plants even recruit predators to prey on the pests that might bother them. It is not quite the same as locking your treasure in a room full of snakes, or poison-tipped darts concealed in cave walls, but it is not far off.

Onion has opted for the chemical defence: tear gas. Rather than tripwires, false floors or carefully balanced pulleys holding back giant boulders, partitions are put up within an onion's cells to separate key chemicals. Isoalliin molecules are stored in one part of the cell, and alliinase enzymes in another. If the cell is damaged, the barrier between the isoalliin and the alliinase enzyme is broken and the two can interact. The alliinase enzyme converts isoalliin into 1-propenesulfenic acid. Then, a second enzyme, lachrymatory factor synthase enzyme (LFS), converts 1-propenesulfenic acid into propanethial-S-oxide, or lachrymatory factor (LF) – the molecule that makes you cry.

LF is a volatile compound that drifts through the air towards a particularly vulnerable part of the body: the eyes. The cornea, the clear covering that protects the eyeball, is densely packed with nerve endings. These run from the eye directly to the brain to alert us to dangers from heat, pressure or chemicals. There are also nerves leading from the brain back to the eye that activate tear glands. When LF reaches our eyes, it automatically sets off our emergency sprinkler system and the tears start to flow.

The search for the solution to stopping the tears has been as long and almost as eventful as the search for the Holy Grail. Some advocate placing a burned match between your teeth on the grounds that the sulphur in the match head will attract the sulphurous LF, but this makes no chemical sense. Holding a wooden spoon in the mouth is equally nonsensical. You could try wearing swimming goggles instead. Blocking the eyes in some way will work, but only up to a point. There are nerve endings in the nose connected to the eyes, so breathing in the oniony aerosols will produce the same, if reduced, effect.

Yet another option to keep your eyes dry may be to get your hands wet. Chopping onions under water will stop the LF reaching your eyes, but may increase the risk of cuts by making the onions more difficult to handle. The same goes for chopping onions inside a bag.

Like Dr Jones trying to work out the cryptic clues that enable him to bypass the booby traps safely, Dr Colin Eady used genetic engineering to slice out the gene for LFS. Without it, no LF can be produced, and no tears either. Sunions are another tearless alternative, created the old-fashioned way through decades of selective breeding. Chopping these onions may not be as adventurous, but few of us will cry over the loss.

$C_3H_5N_3O_9$

Nitroglycerin
A Bigger Bang for Your Buck

As molecules go, nitroglycerin is rather highly strung. It is extremely sensitive and prone to explosive outbursts, and it has been pushed to this peak of anxiety and instability by human interference. Its inclination to fall apart at the least provocation, however, is also its most useful quality.

In 1847, Italian chemist Ascanio Sobrero took innocuous glycerine and decided to make some changes. He replaced some of its hydrogen atoms with nitro groups, a nitrogen with two oxygen atoms attached. The result was nitroglycerin: an oily colourless liquid that was intensely unhappy with itself. The reason for nitroglycerin's dissatisfaction is the way its atoms are arranged. Imagine the worst possible seating plan for an important dinner party, where a group of forceful personalities have been crammed round one small table. Any two characters guaranteed not to get along have been seated next to each other. Tensions will be high. One mistimed sniping comment can quickly descend into an all-out brawl. As with the imaginary diners, the atoms within nitroglycerin take any opportunity to split off from their current neighbours and rearrange themselves into more stable conformations. An increase in temperature, or a slight knock, can flex or shake the molecule,

Nitroglycerin
Oily colourless liquid

Melting Point
13°C (56°F)

Boiling Point
49–60°C (124–140°F)

Molecular Weight
227g/mol

snapping the weaker bonds and bringing atoms closer to their preferred partners. Nitroglycerin easily fragments into new molecules, many of which are gases that rapidly expand thanks to the tremendous amount of heat that is released in the process. All of this happens so quickly it creates an explosion.

Nitroglycerin's sudden and violent breakdowns were too much for Sobrero. Just being around the stuff gave him a headache. He swore off nitroglycerin research and advised others to do the same. Nevertheless, one of his students was undeterred. The young man, a Swede named Alfred Nobel, saw nitroglycerin's destructive potential. It could be a far more powerful alternative to gunpowder, the only explosive available at the time, if it could be controlled. Frequent unplanned explosions did not stop Alfred from opening a nitroglycerin plant with his father, Immanuel. One explosion claimed the lives of five people, including Alfred's brother Emil, and prompted the authorities to ban the Nobels from working within the city limits. Rather than give up, they relocated to a barge anchored on Lake Mälaren. It was here that nitroglycerin was finally brought under control.

What nitroglycerin needed was support, and Alfred gave it in the form of kieselguhr, a very absorbent clay-like material that soaked up and stabilized the liquid nitroglycerin to form a paste. This paste was safe to transport, could be easily moulded and still gave a powerful explosion when detonated. Alfred called it dynamite.

Dynamite proved to be enormously popular in both civil and military settings. Alfred made a fortune. Though he became very wealthy, he was not necessarily happy. Alfred had been plagued by ill health throughout his life. When he developed heart problems, he was prescribed nitroglycerin to relieve his symptoms. The compound that had made him also saved him from the pain of angina.

In 1888, Alfred was alarmed to read his own obituary in a Paris newspaper. In fact, it was his brother Ludvik who had died, but it made him consider how he might be remembered. He decided to leave almost all of his wealth to establish five prizes, to be given to those who 'confer the greatest benefit on mankind' in the fields of peace, literature, chemistry, physics and medicine or physiology.

It is fitting that the 1998 Nobel Prize for Medicine or Physiology was given to Robert Furchgott, Louis Ignarro and Ferid Murad. Their work revealed just how nitroglycerin, the compound that had made such a significant contribution to the funding of the prize and was used to treat its founder, had relieved his pain but also caused some of his headaches. Inside the body, nitroglycerin fragments in a slow and controlled way compared to its behaviour outside. In the endothelial cells that line blood vessels, the molecule breaks up to release nitrous oxide. The nitrous oxide diffuses into the smooth muscle, triggering relaxation and a widening of the blood vessel. The increase in blood flow to the brain can cause the headaches experienced by Nobel, Sobrero and anyone else exposed to large amounts of nitroglycerin. But in the right dose, it primarily affects the veins leading to the heart, blood pressure drops and the heart does not have to work so hard. Once again, nitroglycerin's fragility is, in reality, its strength.

$C_4H_{10}O$

Diethyl Ether
An End to Pain

I would like, if I may, to take you on a strange journey through the layers of your consciousness. *Anaesthesia, or The End of Pain* is a little piece of theatre in five acts. It features Valerius Cordus, a scientist; William Morton, a hero; John Snow, an investigator; Ann Parkinson, a heroine; and a few unconventional partygoers. But at the heart of the story is the strange and seductive diethyl ether, the sweet oil of vitriol, who can cast anyone – man, woman or other – under its spell.

The adventure begins in a sixteenth-century laboratory. In the first act, Valerius Cordus mixes alcohol and sulphuric acid to make a sickly, clawing chemical he names 'sweet oil of vitriol'. Guests arrive. As they inhale the chemical's heady charms, some feel nauseous, while others are intoxicated by the peculiar feelings it brings on.

The party continues into the second act, which takes place in a nineteenth-century ballroom, where our hero, William Morton, is watching events from the sidelines. He notices the guests' eccentric behaviour and realizes it cannot just be down to the alcohol and nibbles. There is something else going on. The partygoers dance and cavort excitedly but their movements become increasingly uncoordinated and eventually they fall to the floor.

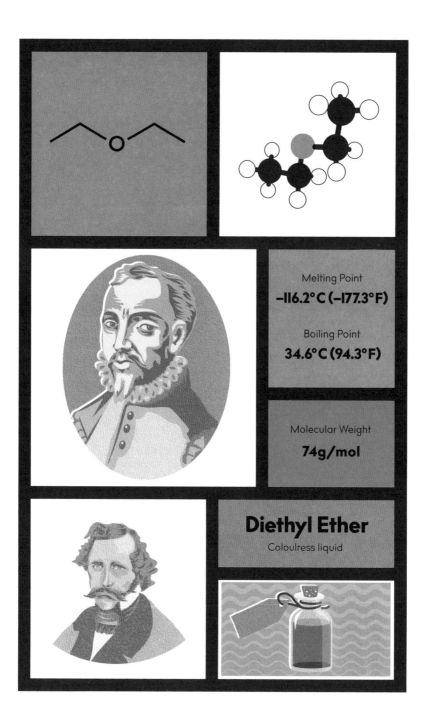

Melting Point
−116.2°C (−177.3°F)

Boiling Point
34.6°C (94.3°F)

Molecular Weight
74g/mol

Diethyl Ether
Coloulress liquid

Any semblance of reality slips away as we progress into act three. It is an early October morning in 1846, in an operating theatre at Massachusetts General Hospital. It is here that the sweet oil of vitriol makes a dramatic entrance and formally introduces itself as diethyl ether (we have been treated to a few cameo appearances already, but they have mostly gone unnoticed). Now, we are helplessly in ether's thrall. An audience, shivering in anticipation, gathers to witness ether's biomedical breakthrough. It is a morning they will remember for a very long time. On the slab is a young Edward Abbott. John Collins Warren, chief surgeon, watches as Morton introduces diethyl ether to the prone Abbott. At a signal from Morton, Warren steps forward and starts to cut away at the tumour on Abbott's jaw. To everyone's disbelief, the patient does not struggle or cry out and seems blissfully unaware of his ordeal. When he recovers, Abbott reassures Warren that he experienced no pain.

It is a surgical triumph, but some of Morton's medical colleagues appear on stage to question ether's behaviour. These Victorian gentlemen assert that pain is a necessary stimulant for preserving life during operations. Without pain, they warn, childbirth would be like sex; the moral dangers of women experiencing absolute pleasure cannot be overstated. But these men are heckled off stage. Why should we not be kept safe from trouble and pain?

The fourth act dives deeper into ether's world and fully realizes its paralysing control. Ether renders an individual unconscious and unflinching, no matter how painful the stimulus. Under ether's influence, some have fantastical dreams, but amnesia is more

Diethyl Ether

common and convenient, given the horrors that are done to them. The experience is difficult to describe. It is not sleep, nor a drunken stupor or death. A new word is needed for this strange new state of being and Morton chooses 'anaesthesia'.

Soon after, John Snow arrives to fill in some of the missing details. He has been investigating ether and found a pattern in its behaviour. Snow reveals to the audience the five stages of anaesthesia: disorientation, excitement or delirium, followed by unconsciousness, surgical anaesthesia and, in the final act, when ether goes too far, death.

The play draws to a close on a sombre note. It is March 1847, and we are in a courtroom. Ether stands in the dock, accused of murder. Under ether's influence, Ann Parkinson had a tumour removed from her thigh. The operation was a success, but Ann died thirty-six hours later having never regained consciousness. Ether tries to explain – there had been no intention to kill, only to relieve pain. The verdict is acquittal, but ether is disgraced. Two other anaesthetics, chloroform and nitrous oxide, seize the opportunity to take over. Chloroform is easier to get along with but proves to be more deadly than ether. Ether remains on the fringes as something for specialists who understand its behaviour and can moderate its excesses.

This little drama once enjoyed an extraordinary run in theatres around the world, but fiery ether has since lost its starring role and taken its final curtain. Since the 1980s, safe, swift and reliable fluorinated hydrocarbons have become the stars of *Anaesthesia* – a cult classic, if you will.

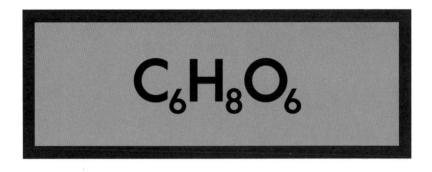

$$C_6H_8O_6$$

Vitamin C
The Scurvy Knave

In 1740, the British hatched a cunning plan. Envious of the wealth Spain was extracting from South America, and with tensions running high between the two nations, they needed to take decisive action. Lord Anson was to lead a flotilla of ships from England, round Cape Horn and up the western coast of South America to capture the Peruvian port of Callao, and the capital Lima, if possible. The Brits would then take Panama, incite a rebellion, capture at least one of Spain's prized galleons, cross the Pacific and take Manila. It was, perhaps, a little ambitious, so Manila was crossed off the list. To achieve the revised set of goals, Anson was to be supplied with six war ships, two support vessels and five hundred troops.

But the troops were not forthcoming, so they turned to Chelsea hospital, home to soldiers unable to join marching regiments through injury, age or mental incapacity. Hearing of the plan, those who could walk out of the hospital did so. Of those who were left, 259 boarded Anson's ships, some on stretchers. The rest were made up of young marines, some of them apparently so raw they had never fired a gun.

The journey started reasonably well. Thereafter, they sometimes had less time to re-provision than they would like because they had to

Vitamin C
White to very pale yellow crystalline powder

Melting Point
190°C (374°F)

Boiling Point
552.7°C (1026.9°F)

Molecular Weight
176g/mol

leave port before the Spanish arrived. And then typhus and dysentery began to run rife through the crew. But it was on approaching Cape Horn that things really started to fall apart. Storms battered the ships, freezing seawater drenched the crew and then the most dread of all things appeared: scurvy.

After six months at sea, the crew were undoubtedly missing dry land. Most of all, they were missing vitamin C. It is a small thing, and you do not need much of it, but unlike most animals, humans cannot make it for themselves. Whatever stocks the crews' bodies had before they left England had long gone and the provisions that were available failed to make up for the loss. Even if their food had not rotted en route, even if they had the opportunity to properly restock, it is unlikely they would have got all the vitamin C they really needed.

The first time fresh fruit and vegetables had been linked with scurvy prevention had been in the sixteenth century, but the concept did not catch on. The idea that a tiny component of food was capable of correcting a deficiency was inconceivable at the time. Making the connection was even more difficult because some foods have more vitamin C than others with no outward indication of which is best. The vitamin content diminishes the longer a food is stored and the same happens when the food is cooked. When a connection was made

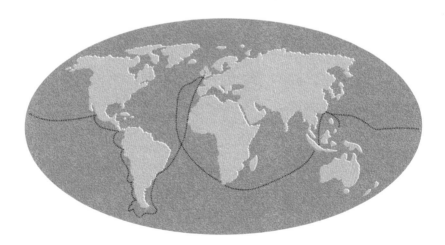

Vitamin C

between citrus fruits and scurvy, it was attributed to their acidic nature. When Lord Anson set sail, rations of lemon or lime juice were still six decades away. Instead, he followed the accepted wisdom of the day and stocked up on 'elixir of vitriol', a mixture of sulphuric acid in alcohol.

No matter how much elixir was dropped into the crews' mouths, their gums would continue to bleed, their joints to swell and bruises to spread across their body. The wounds one crew member had received at the Battle of the Boyne, fifty years earlier, reopened. The callus that had formed over a bone fractured in the battle dissolved, and the bone broke anew. Men who appeared only mildly afflicted lay in their hammocks singing boisterously, but if they got up they dropped dead before reaching the deck.

Vitamin C, or ascorbic acid, has many roles in the body, but the one Lord Anson's crew missed most was its role in adding hydroxyl groups to collagen fibres. Collagen, from the Greek word for glue, is what holds us together. It is in cartilage, tendons, skin, bones, blood vessels, the valves of the heart, and is used by the body to hastily cover and close wounds. Added along specially constructed protein strands, the hydroxyl groups – after modification – allow adjacent fibres to knit together.

After four years and a complete circumnavigation of the globe, Lord Anson limped home with only one thing ticked off his to-do list – the capture of a Spanish galleon. He had more than thirty-four tonnes of silver on board, but only a third of the men he had set sail with.

$C_6H_{12}O_6$

Glucose
Stoking the Furnace

Life is complicated. There are a million different things going on inside us even when, from the outside, we appear to be doing nothing. Our limbs may be still, but there are muscles helping inflate our lungs, push blood round our arteries and veins, and food through our digestive tract. We may not be thinking of anything in particular, but nerves are firing to keep tabs on everything. Every cell has something going on inside it, whether it is dividing, carrying out repairs or just functioning. There is no rest. All this activity requires energy – readily available and easy to use. It is an incredible challenge to meet these complex and ever-changing energy demands, but glucose is an incredible fuel.

All the glucose that keeps us going comes from literal power plants. Chlorophyll, packed into leaves and stems, channels the energy of sunlight into rearranging six carbon dioxide and six water molecules into six oxygen molecules and one of glucose. Around 50 billion tonnes of glucose is generated this way every year, making it the most abundant biomolecule on the planet. It is far more than the plants need for their own energy requirements. Some glucose gets adapted to sweeten fruits that attract animals that can spread the seeds inside them. Some of those glucose molecules are needed for conversion into

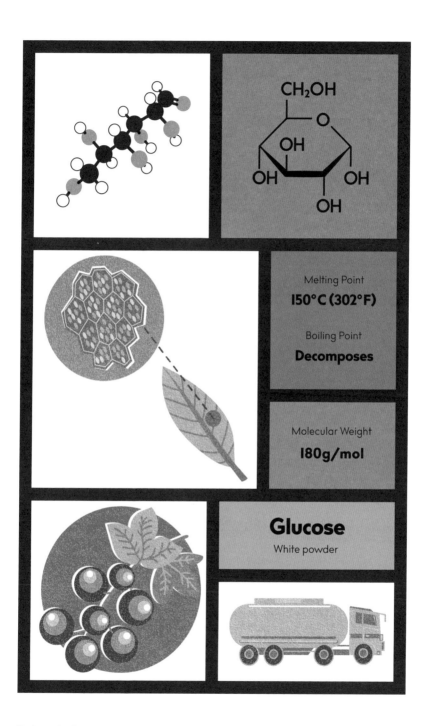

CH₂OH

OH

OH
OH
OH

Melting Point
150°C (302°F)

Boiling Point
Decomposes

Molecular Weight
180g/mol

Glucose
White powder

components of other structures in the plant body. But most of them are strung together in short strands as starch and stashed away. Starch can be an energy stockpile for a rainy day or stored in seeds as a kind of starter pack for new shoots.

Our bodies make great use of the glucose tied up in starch. We break up plant material with our teeth, and enzymes in our mouths chop the starch strands into their individual glucose units. These are absorbed from the gut and distributed to virtually every cell in the body according to its energy needs. The more energy required, the more glucose it uses, and the more mitochondria, the biological furnaces that 'burn' up the glucose to release that energy, are packed into that cell. Red blood cells are the only cells to have no mitochondria, but liver cells have between one and two thousand to keep up the supply of energy needed for its many functions.

The key to releasing energy from glucose is the carbon atoms. There is a lot of energy to be obtained by bonding a carbon atom to an oxygen atom, and slightly less when forming a hydrogen–oxygen bond. It is why we burn hydrocarbons – coal, oil, natural gas – with oxygen from the air to fuel our lives. But glucose molecules come with some oxygen atoms already attached. It means we can extract less energy out of glucose than the equivalent hydrocarbon and there is, therefore, a reduction in output. There are other benefits to having these carbon atoms partly oxidized, however.

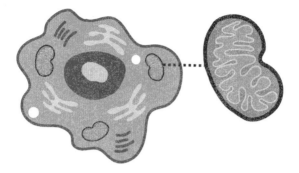

Though hydrocarbons release a lot of energy, biology transports its energy molecules around not in tankers and trains and pipes, but dissolved in water. Water and hydrocarbons do not mix. Adding oxygen groups to the crown of carbon atoms in a glucose molecule attracts water that pulls it into solution. With its cushion of water, glucose is swept into the bloodstream and delivered to cells around the body. The mitochondria furnaces inside the cells add more oxygen atoms, delivered from the lungs, to release energy and belch out carbon dioxide, which is returned to the lungs as waste.

But those oxygen groups that help glucose dissolve hang onto water molecules rather too well. Glucose is so good at holding onto water, that it can change the pressure inside cells and damage them. A sudden influx of glucose from a meal can be dangerous. The answer is to use those same oxygen hooks to string glucose molecules together into insoluble strands and wrap them around a protein like a molecular pompom. The process of converting glucose to glycogen, mediated by insulin, is how the body can keep blood sugar levels under control. And the glycogen pompoms can easily be unravelled between meals or in response to changing energy demands throughout the body. What glucose loses in available energy, it more than makes up for with its ease of transport and adaptable storage. Glucose molecules are brilliantly packaged biological fuel.

$C_7H_5NO_3S$

Saccharin
Licking the Spoon

Chemistry is often likened to cooking. Both involve following a recipe, mixing ingredients, lots of stirring, boiling and baking. Keeping your hands clean is also important in both activities, though they should be washed before cooking and after handling chemicals. The key difference between the two is that, no matter how good your product looks or smells, a chemist should never, ever lick the spoon.

Today there are rules, protocols and best practices to keep people safe when working in a chemical laboratory, but in the past things were a little more lax. In 1878, Constantine Fahlberg was working with Ira Remsen in a laboratory at the University of Baltimore. Their research was into coal tar – black, oily residues that contain lots of interesting chemicals, if you do not mind getting your hands dirty fishing them out. Fahlberg was definitely willing to get his hands dirty, but it would seem he was less than scrupulous about washing them afterwards.

Sitting down to dinner after a hard day at the chemistry bench, Fahlberg noticed his bread roll had a very sweet crust. His wife said her roll tasted just as it should, so he deduced the unusual flavour must be due to a chemical he had handled earlier in the day. Tasting his way around his bench, he identified the culprit as ortho-sulfobenzoic acid

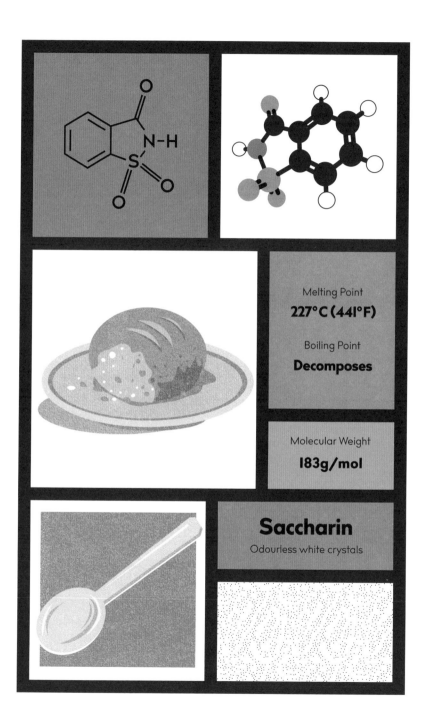

Melting Point
227°C (441°F)

Boiling Point
Decomposes

Molecular Weight
183g/mol

Saccharin
Odourless white crystals

imide. The name was shortened to saccharin and the discovery of a compound 300 times sweeter than sugar was announced by the two chemists in a scientific paper. Fahlberg also took out a patent on the production of the chemical, but failed to include Remsen, the more senior scientist in the lab, in the document. It was something Remsen never forgave him for, though apparently the animosity was not down to the money Fahlberg made from the patent, but the failure to give proper recognition for Remsen's contribution.

Fahlberg began manufacturing saccharin for use as a safe food additive. It gave the illusion of sugar, but with a fraction of the quantity and none of the calories – a boon for diabetics and dieters. In fact, virtually every saccharin molecule passes through the body to be excreted in urine unchanged. The only apparent downside was a bitter, metallic aftertaste that was difficult to mask.

More sweet-tasting chemicals were discovered by more careless chemists as time went on. In 1937, one chemist was smoking in the lab, a nasty habit, and particularly so when surrounded by highly flammable solvents. Having left a cigarette smouldering on the bench, he noticed a sweet taste when he picked it up to take a drag. This led to the discovery of cyclamate sweetener. In 1965, another chemist licked his finger to pick up a piece of paper and discovered aspartame. Neither compound was as sweet as saccharin, but aspartame did not have the

disagreeable aftertaste. Cyclamate, however, was the least sweet of the lot, though still ten or twenty times sweeter than sugar, but has been banned in several places over safety concerns.

What seemed to be fantastic culinary discoveries took a while to find their market. The use of saccharin and other sweeteners only started to increase during the Second World War. Sugar imports from the Caribbean to Britain were prey to German U-boats, restricting how much could get through. Strict sugar rationing was enforced, but people did not lose their sweet tooth. Saccharin could be used to fill the gap. There was a further boost in the 1960s and 1970s, when the diet industry took off and it could be used as a sugar substitute.

Now, low- or zero-calorie drinks are commonplace. Fears of side-effects have proved unfounded. Improved formulations and recipes mean our taste buds can scarcely tell the difference between sugar-free and the real thing. When baking, we can lick the spoon without worrying about the extra calories. Interestingly, however, not everyone is fooled. Bees and butterflies cannot be tricked into accepting saccharin as a sugar substitute.

Stricter health-and-safety practice in chemistry laboratories perhaps means we are missing out on many new exciting flavours. But it also means there are fewer fires and not as many chemists ending up in accident and emergency departments. When it comes to a safe working environment, we should accept no substitutes.

$C_8H_{10}N_4O_2$

Caffeine
A Mind-Altering Substance

In 1948, students in the zoology department at the University of Tübingen were tasked with filming spiders constructing their webs. The group sat up four nights in a row patiently waiting for the spiders to start spinning. As each long night dragged on towards morning, the students would doze, only to wake a few hours later and find the webs had been spun while they slept. The sleep-deprived students decided to consult a colleague, Peter Witt, a pharmacologist. Could something be given to the spiders to make them reschedule their web-spinning to a more convenient time?

Witt was researching the effects of different substances on humans and had no idea what their effect might be on arachnids, so he gave the students samples of sedatives, hallucinogens and stimulants to try out. But no matter what drug was tried, the spiders still constructed their webs at the same uncivilized hour. Instead, the effects of working under the influence of psychoactive drugs showed in the webs they produced.

With most drugs, the spiders could keep things together enough to produce the basic framework of a web, the radial spokes. It was spinning the spirals of silk threads that connect the spokes where things fell apart. Benzedrine made the spiders stagger round like drunkards,

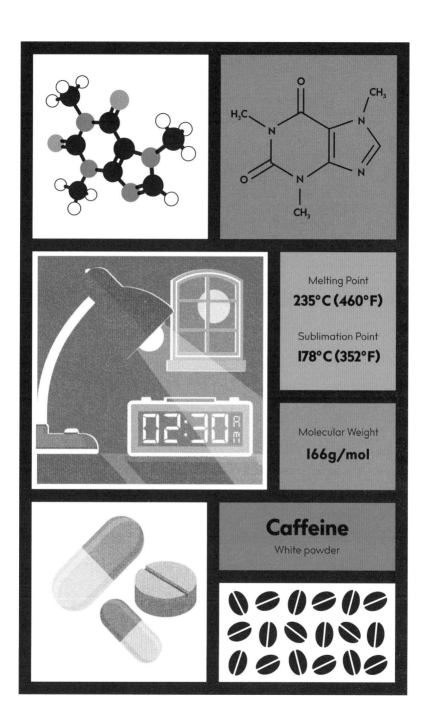

Melting Point
235°C (460°F)

Sublimation Point
178°C (352°F)

Molecular Weight
166g/mol

Caffeine
White powder

creating zigzag patterns where there should be neat circles. With scopolamine, they lost all sense of direction and wandered off to add silk strands wherever their eight drug-addled legs decided to take them. Some webs were so strange, one can only wonder at the state of the spider that created them. These webs had no central hub and no radial spokes, only random threads and connections that looked more like crazy paving. And the drug that sent these spiders completely off their webs was caffeine.

Around 80 per cent of the world's human population regularly uses caffeine with little or no concern. We usually think of it as a mild stimulant safe enough to take in multiple doses over the course of a day. However, it is a potent psychoactive drug. Caffeine molecules block receptors where adenosine should dock. Adenosine regulates the release of other chemicals that stimulate our nerves, making us more wakeful, alert and focused. Caffeine increases the amount of dopamine in the brain, making us feel good, and cranks up our metabolism, hence its use in diet aids. On the downside, caffeine speeds up our heart rate and increases blood flow to the kidneys, meaning more urine is produced. All of which is fine . . . in moderation.

Your morning coffee will deliver 80–120 mg of caffeine, depending on whether you prefer instant or fresh ground. A cup of tea or can of cola can deliver 40 mg of caffeine. Chocolate can also help to top up your caffeine levels. But as more caffeine molecules are introduced into the body, more receptors are blocked and more nerve stimulants are

Caffeine

released. Caffeinism usually kicks in at around ten to fifteen cups of coffee a day. It can cause nervousness, irritability, insomnia, headaches and heart palpitations. A lethal caffeine intake would be 5–10g, or somewhere above fifty cups of coffee a day.

Our bodies treat caffeine molecules as the toxic invaders that they are by dismantling and getting rid of them. Carbon atoms are snipped off to transform caffeine into theophylline and paraxanthine, which have much the same effect on the body, prolonging the buzz long after we have finished the cup. But eventually these compounds are also broken down and cleared from our system. While work is done to eliminate the toxins, effort is also made to minimize their impact on the body. Regular exposure to caffeine causes the body to increase the number of receptors for it, so adenosine can carry on functioning without caffeine getting in the way. It takes a few days to develop a tolerance. During periods of abstinence, such as the hours of sleep, the number of receptors decreases slightly, making the first cup of coffee in the morning the most potent. After a few days caffeine free, gulping down your once habitual dose will have a much bigger impact.

The spiders in the 1948 experiment were probably experiencing caffeine for the first time and the impact it had on them could be seen in their webs. It had no less a dramatic effect on Peter Witt, who promptly gave up his human research and turned his attention to drugged spiders.

$$C_8H_{11}N$$

Phenylethylamine
The Feel-Good Factor

Moctezuma II was an aficionado of *chocolatl*. There are stories that he drank sixty cups a day and nothing else. The Europeans who tried it were sceptical. If you could get past the frothy, oily scum floating on the surface, you would find a bitter liquid underneath. But Moctezuma had expanded and developed his Aztec Empire to unprecedented size, sophistication and wealth. He was also said to have fifty wives and one hundred children. Could this be down to his drinking habits?

Moctezuma was not alone is his love for *chocolatl*. The oldest known accounts of the drink were written by the Maya in 400 CE, though something similar was being prepared as long ago as 1900 BCE. The Maya recipe started with the fruit of the cacao tree. The large pods were split open to expose the fleshy interior, allowing the sweet, white pulp that surrounded the seeds to ferment. The sugar converted into alcohol, which slowly oxidized to acetic acid. The acid killed the seeds and helped to release flavour molecules. After a few days, the seeds were removed and dried, allowing the acetic acid to evaporate. The seeds were then ground into a paste and mixed with water and spices. The resulting mix was served hot with a little wooden stick for beating the fatty and watery components into a froth before drinking.

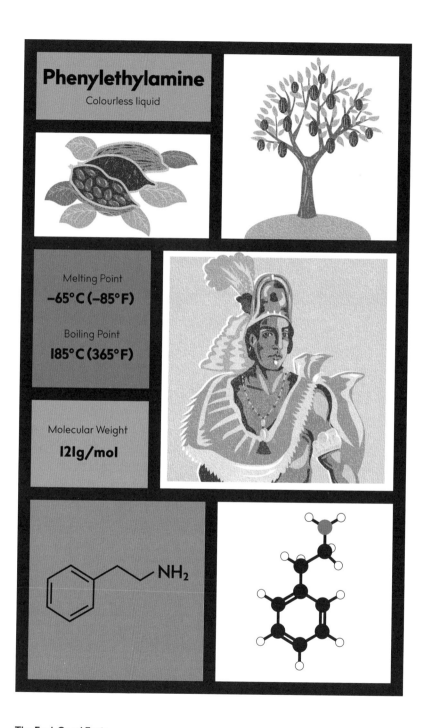

Phenylethylamine
Colourless liquid

Melting Point
−65°C (−85°F)

Boiling Point
185°C (365°F)

Molecular Weight
121g/mol

NH_2

When the Aztec Empire expanded into Maya territory, the Aztecs enthusiastically adopted the drink but preferred imbibing it cold. Consumption increased among Aztec men (women were barred from drinking it), but they struggled to cultivate their own cacao trees. So, duties levied on the Maya were made payable in cocoa seeds and they became part of the economy.

When the Europeans arrived during Moctezuma's reign, they were happy to trade in cocoa seeds with the locals. They were, however, less inclined to consume them – at least until their own provisions started to run dry. Some came to like the drink's refreshing flavour and took the recipe back home with them, along with some supplies of cocoa. There was a great deal of interest in everything that was brought back from the New World. *Chocolatl* proved to be particularly popular at the Spanish royal court. With everyone wanting to copy royalty, once sweetened to suit the European palate, chocolate-drinking really took off. Physicians recommended it for soothing the stomach. Casanova rated it more highly than champagne for increasing ardour. Such big claims may be overblown, but cocoa's enduring popularity is undeniable. In the centuries since, cocoa has been refined into bonbons and bars, and added to cakes and other consumables that bear little resemblance to the original *chocolatl* of the Americas. Demand for chocolate has created a multibillion-dollar industry. Maybe there really was something in Moctezuma's drink after all.

Phenylethylamine

In truth there were lots of things in Moctezuma's drink. Quite apart from the vanilla and chilli flavouring, and the cornmeal that helped the fatty and watery components to mix, the main ingredient, cocoa, contains more than five hundred compounds. Of these hundreds of chemicals there are three that have a significant effect on the human body, and specifically the central nervous system. The first two, caffeine and theobromine, are chemically very similar and produce much the same stimulating effect. However, if there was a special something in cocoa, the most likely candidate is the third of these neurologically active compounds: phenylethylamine.

Formed during the fermentation stage of cocoa processing, phenylethylamine is structurally similar to a range of compounds that includes amphetamines, psychedelics and antidepressant drugs. Phenylethylamine is made naturally inside the body but in quantities too tiny to produce an amphetamine-like response. But, if Moctezuma's dietary habits are to be believed, he would have been getting a considerable boost. He would certainly need it to appreciate any benefits from the phenylethylamine he was ingesting because it is rapidly broken down into inactive phenylacetic acid in the gut.

As an explanation of our love of cocoa-based confectionery, the effects of phenylethylamine are interesting but probably overblown. I will admit that I am biased, but chocolate is, nevertheless, the food of the gods. Carl Linnaeus named cocoa's parent plant *Theobroma cacao*, from the Greek *theo* for 'god' and *broma* for 'food'. Its seeds have been used for ceremonial purposes, traded as a currency, drunk as an aphrodisiac, sold as a medicine and eaten to give comfort for at least 4,000 years.

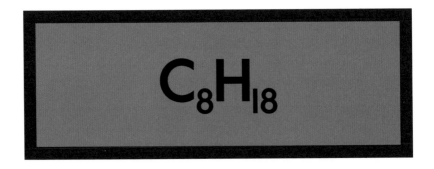

Octane
The Need for Speed

One of the greatest love affairs of the twentieth century is on the rocks. It started so well. We were seduced by an easy-going, very available war hero with huge earning potential and powerful friends. Marriage to this molecule offered a glamorous lifestyle, a comfortable place to live and travel to far-flung places. There have been many happy decades together, but cracks have appeared. Could this be the end of a long and beautiful relationship?

Hydrocarbons first charmed us back in the late nineteenth century. This family of compounds, made of only hydrogen and carbon, came from good old stock. Sure, they were crude at first, when they were all jumbled together, but with a little effort they could be refined. The family stretches to several branches: the alkenes, the aromatics and the alkanes. All have excellent qualities, but the alkanes found a special place in our hearts. They have strong carbon backbones, just like the other hydrocarbons, but they have more hydrogen atoms studded along their backbones than the others. This maximum ratio of hydrogen to carbon atoms gives them a stable and even temperament. Oxygen, however, given a nudge, is apt to provoke them and, once triggered, the reaction can be explosive. This fiery temper has the potential

Melting Point
−56.8°C (−70.2°F)

Boiling Point
125.6°C (258.1°F)

Molecular Weight
114g/mol

Octane
Colourless liquid

to create power, and with power comes money. Alkane's prospects looked extremely good. In the early twentieth century, an alliance was formed with a select number of alkanes. The shorter members of the family, those with a handful of carbon atoms, proved to be particularly amenable. They were liquids that were easy to store and transport, but still easy to vaporize and ignite. This selection of short-chain alkanes filled an ever-increasing number of petrol tanks, though one individual stood out among the others.

Octane, named for the eight carbon atoms it contains, comes in two forms, like non-identical twins: one with all eight carbons strung in a row, and another with carbons branching off from a shortened carbon spine. The straight-chain twin was a little explosive, but iso-octane, its shapely, branched sibling, was a smooth operator, the real high-flyer of the family. Iso-octane burned evenly, heating the gas inside combustion engines to give a steady pressure that improved vehicle performance. It became the standard measure for fuel performance and was given a score of 100 on the octane rating.

Methods were developed to crack long-chain hydrocarbons into smaller, more attractive pieces and reform their carbons into the desirable branched arrangement. In 1940, a new blend of high-octane fuel gave the Allies' aeroplanes greater horsepower and bested the German aircraft that had out-flown them only weeks earlier. Octane was a Battle of Britain hero. We were completely won over.

'High octane' became a phrase often on our lips, to describe anything fast-paced and exciting. Wedding ourselves to octane and its family gave us access to a whole new world. Thanks to hydrocarbons' influence we could move to bigger houses in greener areas and enjoy drive-ins and drive-thrus. We could travel further, faster, more comfortably and cheaply. We seemed settled in our suburban lives.

The first warning that all was not perfect came in the 1970s. Life with hydrocarbons suddenly became very expensive. The crisis passed, but it opened our eyes to some of hydrocarbons' flaws. In recent decades, our comfortable lives together are becoming increasingly uncomfortable. Suburbs can feel remote and commuting can try our patience. Oil also comes with chemical baggage that we initially overlooked. Nitrogen and sulphur compounds were always tagging along and causing problems. The power of hydrocarbon's reaction with oxygen remains appealing, but the resulting pollution is increasingly difficult to live with. All the little unpleasantries, the smog, the greenhouse gases, have built up into a nasty atmosphere.

It might be difficult to imagine life apart, but as the cost of living with hydrocarbons becomes ever higher, our eyes have started to wander to other prospective partners. There have been flirtations with ethanol, hydrogen and LPG (liquefied petroleum gas), but it seems electricity may ultimately win our hearts with offers of a better, cleaner long-term relationship.

Divorce is likely, on grounds of irreconcilable differences. Extricating ourselves from our relationship with octane is going to be messy, protracted and will undoubtedly involve expensive lawyers. After living in each other's pockets for so long, our lives seem inextricably entangled. Complete separation may be impossible, but we need to spend a lot less time in each other's company for everyone's sake.

$$C_8H_{20}Pb$$

Tetraethyl Lead
A Bumpy Ride

Tetraethyl lead is a bad influence. It is an example to be held up as a lesson in how not to do things. Here follows a cautionary tale of madness, death and fast cars, all washed down with some excellent wines. Buckle up, it is going to be a bumpy ride.

Created in Germany, in 1854, tetraethyl lead is four greasy ethyl groups of two carbon and five hydrogen atoms each, attached to a central lead atom. The combination makes an already toxic metal easier to absorb through our oily skin and into the fatty parts of our body. It was a bad beginning, but the dangers were recognized and this awful compound was avoided for more than sixty years. Nevertheless, not everyone was put off.

In 1921, a fast-growing enthusiasm for cars was being tempered by the engine 'knocking' and occasionally shuddering and shaking to a halt. The cause of the uncomfortable ride and expensive engine damage was the fuel being used to power the vehicles. The mix of hydrocarbons in the petrol available at that time burned too fast, out of sync with the pistons, and resulted in an inefficient and uncoordinated engine. It was a problem, and Thomas Midgley Jr thought tetraethyl lead was the solution.

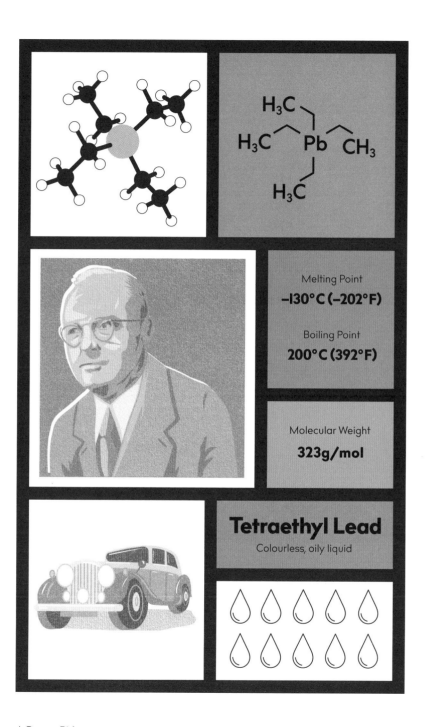

H_3C

H_3C — Pb — CH_3

H_3C

Melting Point
−130°C (−202°F)

Boiling Point
200°C (392°F)

Molecular Weight
323g/mol

Tetraethyl Lead
Colourless, oily liquid

Midgley found that adding a dash of inexpensive tetraethyl lead to the gas tank boosted a car's performance. The lead helped lubricate valves, preventing wear and tear in the engines. The four ethyl groups blended with the other hydrocarbons in the fuel to help it burn more smoothly. Concerns about high toxicity were waved away. Motorists were assured they need not worry about the tiny amount of lead compound in their tank, as it would be diluted in the fuel and dispersed in the engine's exhaust. It was a very different story for those making the tetraethyl lead, or 'looney gas' as it became known among the workers at the Standard Oil Refinery in New Jersey. They forgot their colleagues' names, staggered around and snatched at invisible insects in the air. Some had to be bundled into straitjackets. In one week, in September 1924, five died of lead poisoning.

Reports of these distressing events started to appear in newspapers and so a press conference was called to address the growing concerns. Midgley spoke to journalists while pouring tetraethyl lead over his

Tetraethyl Lead

hands and holding a beaker of the liquid under his nose for a full minute. He claimed it was safe to do this every day without ill effects despite knowing full well that it was not. He had personally suffered lead poisoning from his work with tetraethyl lead only the year before.

Questions were asked about alternatives to lead compounds, but Midgley was adamant: there simply were none. This was also a lie. He knew ethanol also successfully prevented the knocking problem, but it was not as profitable. By the 1960s, all cars in the United States were running on leaded petrol. Tetramethyl lead slowly replaced tetraethyl lead, but the amount of lead in fuel increased. In 1973, it reached a peak of 2.2 grams of lead in every gallon of gasoline, amounting to 200,000 tonnes every year.

Lead started to appear in unexpected places – in lake sediment and Arctic snow. In 1994, French chemist Ryszard Lobinski analysed Châteauneuf-du-Pape wine made from grapes grown at the junction of two motorways in the Rhône region of France. As traffic had built up over the years, so had the amount of lead in the wine, reaching a maximum in 1978. The fact that this year was considered to be one of the best vintages was not a coincidence. The lead acetate it formed tasted great but could cause mild lead poisoning. More worryingly, other research linked poor school performance with higher levels of lead in the blood.

Leaded petrol became persona non grata, but not for the reasons you might think. Legislation was introduced to clean up the air and the car industry had to do its bit. Their solution was the catalytic converter, which reduced the number of pollutants in car exhaust. But these catalytic converters were poisoned by lead. The long-ignored alternative anti-knock agents were finally pressed into action. By 1980, most industrial nations had switched to unleaded petrol. Some have suggested a drop in crime rates in the 1990s is linked. Algeria, the last nation still using leaded petrol, finally exhausted its stocks in 2021, a century after it was first used. Learning our lesson took a long time.

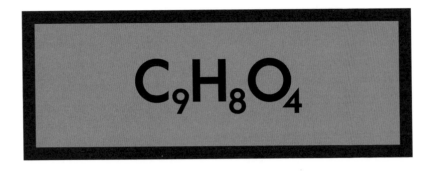

Acetylsalicylic Acid
A Nice Cup of Tea

It is a truth universally acknowledged that a person in possession of a fever must be in want of a cup of tea. At least, that is the case in Britain and Ireland, where tea's therapeutic properties are considered second to none. Feeling sad, in shock, too cold, too hot, a little under the weather – tea is the answer. The tea that Reverend Edward Stone offered to his feverish parishioners in the English town of Chipping Norton was more efficacious than most.

One day, in the late 1750s, the Reverend Stone was walking by the river and reflecting on the damp environs that produced so many agues and fevers among his congregation. Believing that 'many natural maladies carry their cures along with them', perhaps, he thought, the willows growing so abundantly on the banks of the river would provide a cure for those fevers. He chewed a little of their bark and noticed a bitter flavour – as bitter as the cinchona bark known to cure ague.

Today, thanks to a greater scientific understanding, we know that if two substances taste similar it does not mean they will share similar medicinal properties. We also know that the source of ague, or malaria, was the mosquitoes breeding in the water, not the water itself. And, though nature has provided us with many medical miracles, there is

Acetylsalicylic Acid

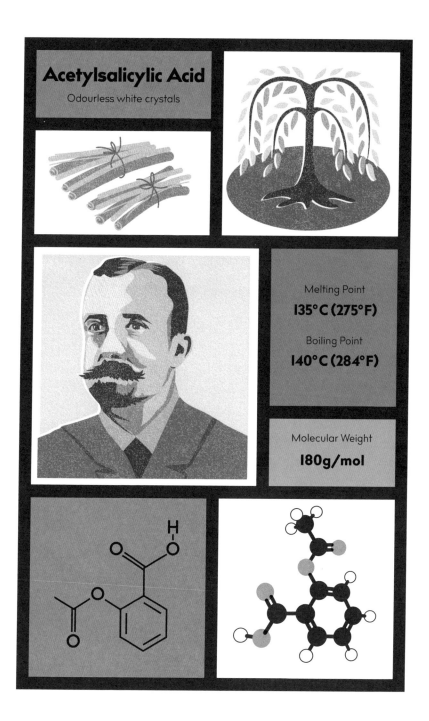

Acetylsalicylic Acid

Odourless white crystals

Melting Point
135°C (275°F)

Boiling Point
140°C (284°F)

Molecular Weight
180g/mol

no guarantee a cure will be located conveniently alongside the cause of disease. But it all made perfect sense at the time.

So, Stone collected a bag full of willow bark, dried it and ground it to dust. When he was himself taken with a fever, he swallowed some of the powder and marvelled at how much better it made him feel. From then on, if any of his congregation became struck down with a similar affliction, he would administer the bark at four-hourly intervals, washed down with water, a little beer or, of course, tea, until the person recovered. Stone tested his treatment on approximately fifty locals, with excellent results. Full of confidence in his willow bark remedy, he wrote to the president of the Royal Society:

> *My Lord,*
> *Among the many useful discoveries, which this age hath made, there are very few which better deserve the attention of the public than what I am going to lay before your lordship.*

It was a bold claim, especially as he was far from the first to make these observations. Humans have been using bark extracts for thousands of years and across the world to treat pain and fever. But Stone was right that it deserved the attention of the public because, unlike many ancient herbal remedies, this one had real potential benefits, all thanks to salicylic acid.

Salicylic acid is a natural hormone that helps plants grow and defend themselves against pathogens. It might be present as a salicylate salt or tethered to a glucose molecule to make salicin. Pure salicylic acid was isolated in the 1820s from meadowsweet, a herb known in folk medicine for its pain-relieving properties. The acid proved to be

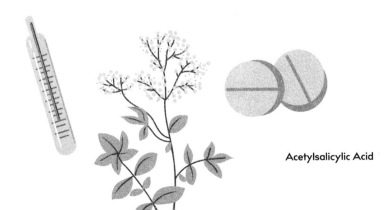

Acetylsalicylic Acid

effective in reducing fever, but it has a foul taste and the painfully irritating habit of causing bleeding and ulceration. Such harsh behaviour needed a little refinement.

In 1897, the chemist Felix Hoffmann added an acetyl group to salicylic acid to see how it would change its medicinal properties. The extra two carbon and five hydrogen atoms dramatically reduced its most irritating qualities while retaining its best features. Given the commercial name aspirin, acetylsalicylic acid went on to be the most successful drug of all time.

Aspirin blocks enzymes that make prostaglandins, a family of chemicals with many roles throughout the body. When the body is injured or invaded by pathogens, it produces an excess of prostaglandins, causing inflammation, fever and transmitting pain signals to the brain. Acetylsalicylic acid also inhibits another family of chemicals, the thromboxanes that cause blood platelets to aggregate. In appropriate doses aspirin can therefore protect people from dangerous blood clots. Though aspirin targets no specific disease, it alleviates the symptoms of many.

But aspirin is not everyone's cup of tea. Prostaglandins also protect cells that line the stomach, which is why aspirin can irritate us. Preventing blood clotting can also result in bleeding. And in some people aspirin provokes an allergic reaction. Affected people have to avoid not just the drug, but plants and foods that can be rich in aspirin's parent compounds. Unfortunately, this can mean missing out on tea, which happens to be rich in salicylates.

$C_9H_{13}NO_3$

Adrenaline
The Warning Sign

Before embarking on our journey into life, we must all pay attention to the emergency procedures. The world can be a dangerous place, full of unexpected and unpredictable threats. Thankfully, we have an inbuilt emergency plan to protect us from the worst. It may not be printed out and laminated like the emergency instructions tucked into the back of every aeroplane seat, but it is as carefully choreographed as the cabin crew's demonstrations before takeoff.

Complex things, like aeroplanes or humans, need sensors and detectors to check everything is running smoothly. Just like an aeroplane, we have ways of monitoring the fuel and oxygen levels onboard and have big windows at the front to look for signs of danger. With constant feedback from our nerves, we can make subtle adjustments to maintain the status quo, allowing us to relax and enjoy a film or a snack on our journey through life. But without a system that can rapidly respond to hazards and potential harm, that journey can be cut short. In life we have sirens and flashing lights to alert us; in the body we have adrenaline.

Should a red warning sign light up on the cockpit console, the co-pilot will point it out to the captain, who then initiates the emergency

Adrenaline

White powder or granules

Melting Point
211.5°C (412°F)

Boiling Point
215°C (419°F)

Molecular Weight
183g/mol

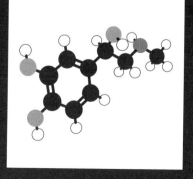

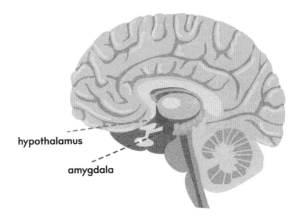

hypothalamus

amygdala

procedure. Alarms and more flashing lights are activated throughout the aircraft and down on the ground in the control tower. This is the signal for everyone – passengers, crew, airport staff, emergency responders – to go about their different duties. Without even knowing what the danger is, or how it might affect anyone, seat belts can be fastened, runways cleared and ambulances dispatched – just in case.

If we perceive a threat, say something spotted out of the cockpit windows that are our eyes, the amygdala in the brain activates the hypothalamus, which releases hormones to activate the adrenal glands, located just above the kidneys. The adrenaline (or epinephrine) that these glands release into the bloodstream is the alarm that sounds throughout the body. These adrenaline molecules dock at receptors in the sympathetic nervous system, a subset of nerves involved in the automatic everyday running of the body. The nerves connect to different cells in different organs and tissues that will each respond to the emergency signal in their own predetermined way.

Activities are quickly reprioritized. With no time for the distraction of an in-flight film, or to savour our snack, we need to focus on the emergency at hand. Adrenaline tells the digestive system to scale down its activities; the drinks trolley is stowed away. Breathing is intensified; oxygen masks fall from the ceiling. We switch to emergency fuel reserves. Blood sugar spikes as glucose is released from the liver to combine with the oxygen being sucked in through the lungs. The heart beats faster and blood vessels leading to the heart, lungs, brain and muscles are dilated to keep them fuelled, alert and ready to act – like the crew busily clearing gangways and checking seatbelts, and the pilots talking to the control tower. And just as passengers adopt the brace position, blood vessels near the skin constrict to minimize damage in the event of injury.

Down on the ground, medical staff grab stocks of bandages and pain killers. In a similar way, the body ramps up production of fibrin, a compound that helps the blood clot if a blood vessel is damaged, and endorphines that dial down our perception of pain. Nerves that control our irises open up the pupil so the maximum visual information can be gathered and the danger assessed. The pilots in the cockpit check their dials and people on the ground pull out binoculars scanning the approaching aircraft for signs of smoke or damage.

Hopefully the plane lands safely, and whatever we glimpsed out of the corner of our eye turns out to be innocuous. A rapid response is essential, even if the threat turns out to be nothing, but that response has to be scaled down quickly. Emergency procedures burn up resources at an astonishing rate, putting stress on the system. In the body, the side products of increased respiration can damage cells. An emergency on board an aircraft, no matter how small, holds up the normal running of an airport. It is disruptive and stressful, but adrenaline helps keep us safe rather than sorry.

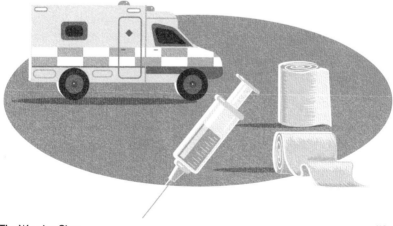

$$C_{10}H_{14}N_2$$

Nicotine
Mr Nice ... But Nasty

If nicotine were a person, it would be the charismatic front man of the notorious tobacco gang: a manipulative molecule with no scruples but a lot of charm; there to distract us while some of the more unpleasant members of its gang do terrible things to us. Despite its obvious downsides, we have struggled to disassociate ourselves from this nasty compound. Instead, we have separated nicotine from its undesirable associates and it is us who are now manipulating the molecule to suit our purposes.

Humans have been smoking tobacco for thousands of years. In the Americas, a pipe of dried tobacco leaves was lit among friends or to close a deal. It also had its uses alleviating aches and the leaves were occasionally applied to the skin as a poultice. When Europeans arrived in the New World, they embraced tobacco and smoking with enthusiasm. In 1560, the French ambassador to Portugal sent tobacco samples to King François II, in Paris, recommending they be snuffed up the royal nose to relieve his recurring headaches. The ambassador, Jean Nicot, was rewarded with the title de Villemain and his name became attached to the tobacco plant, *Nicotiana tabacum*, as well as its principal addictive compound: nicotine. With royal patronage, and a

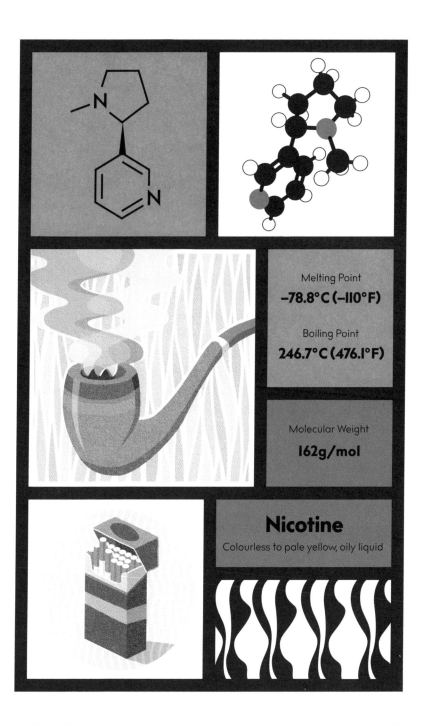

Melting Point
−78.8°C (−110°F)

Boiling Point
246.7°C (476.1°F)

Molecular Weight
162g/mol

Nicotine
Colourless to pale yellow, oily liquid

growing reputation for curing everything from chilblains to carbuncles, ever-increasing quantities of tobacco were shipped east, as millions more Africans were taken west to work tobacco plantations as slaves. People got rich off the back of exploitation, cruelty and nicotine's lies.

Nicotine is an oily customer. It also dissolves in water, giving it access to our bodies through our greasy skin, watery mouth and humid lungs. We have found many ways to acquaint ourselves with its charms, by chewing, sniffing and smoking tobacco. Smoking is the fastest way to get to know this compound. Within seven seconds of a puff on a cigarette, cigar or pipe, nicotine is in your brain docking in nicotinic receptors and playing on your nerves.

At first, nicotine stimulates but, as the amount increases, it acts as a depressant. It helps us concentrate, increases our ability to learn, counteracts our craving for sweet foods and, by increasing the amount of dopamine in our brain, reduces anxiety. It can buck us up or calm us down, but it cannot cure us of any of the maladies it was once recommended for. And, while nicotine distracts us with its myriad tricks, the rest of the chemicals in its tobacco gang can ransack our lungs and maraud through the rest of our body via our circulatory system. There are at least three thousand chemical members of this gang, some of them with very unsavoury reputations. There are those that can poison us quickly, and others that can kill us slowly with cancer. It is easy to turn a blind eye to the rather dubious chemical company nicotine keeps because we like it, and it is gone before we can grow tired of it.

About two hours after tobacco smoke arrives in our lungs, half of the nicotine has been eliminated from our body. Smoking leaves us with a bit of a cough, maybe a sore throat, perhaps even the shakes, but most of all it leaves behind a longing for nicotine's charming company. It produces no euphoria, or even much pleasure, sensations most associated with addictive compounds, but nicotine is certainly addictive. Like the 1960s stars that partied with gangland bosses, and the media that interviewed and photographed them, we can conveniently overlook a few things. For some, the disagreeable side of the tobacco gang are worth putting up with for the chance to hang around with a cool compound like nicotine.

In the past, tobacco companies deliberately added more nicotine to their cigarettes to increase addiction and therefore sales. Nicotine is now used as the lure to entice people away from smoking. Added to chewing gum, vapes and patches, nicotine delivers some of the desirable qualities of smoking, but without the rest of the tobacco gang to cause problems. But, do not be deceived. Nicotine is not very nice.

Nicotine can be a swift and efficient killer. Too much of it will strain the nerves it interacts with to the point of convulsions, collapse and death. These lethal qualities were once thought perfect for killing insects. It could also accidentally, and sometimes intentionally, kill humans. Neonicotinoids, the modified derivatives of nicotine, are less toxic to humans but remain an indiscriminate danger to insects, both friends and foes. We still find nicotine charming, but we have learned to treat it with caution.

$$C_{10}H_{18}O_2$$

9-Oxo-2-Decenoic Acid
The Language of Bees

Rumours spread among the workers that the old queen was dying. There were hints and suggestions that she was losing her power over them. The ladies-in-waiting, those who tended to the queen's every need, were the first to spot the signs of weakness and they spread the news to everyone else. There was no outpouring of grief, no revolution, but a quiet acknowledgement that soon there would have to be a new queen and preparations should be made.

The workers started to build new nurseries, slightly bigger than usual and more fitting for a royal offspring. Though the queen had many identical children, a few were selected for special attention. These princesses knew they were destined for greater things and hummed and buzzed from within their superior accommodation to let everyone else know they were special. As they grew, the princesses were treated to a diet fit for a queen. They enjoyed unstinting supplies of royal jelly, whereas everyone else ate ordinary bee bread. The jelly helped the teenage princesses grow big and strong and regal.

The teens stomped about the hive, trampling workers underfoot and making so much noise that no one could doubt their superiority. Each of the handful of royal pretenders sought out their rivals to challenge

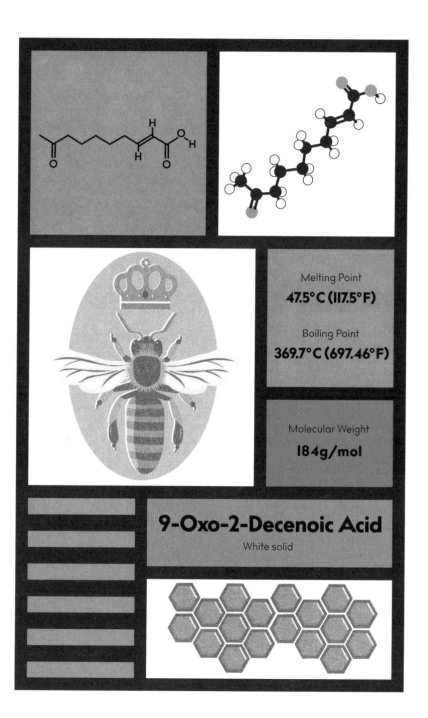

Melting Point
47.5°C (117.5°F)

Boiling Point
369.7°C (697.46°F)

Molecular Weight
184g/mol

9-Oxo-2-Decenoic Acid
White solid

them to a fight to the death. After much mauling and stinging, only one candidate remained. The new virgin queen had asserted her dominance and began to mature into her new role. Her body started to produce pheromones, in particular 9-oxo-2-decenoic acid, or 9ODA, a relatively simple molecule that would perform many complex tasks over the rest of her royal life.

Meanwhile, the old queen continued to decline. Sensing her failing health, and with a new queen ready to take her place, the colony took decisive action. A cluster of bees surrounded the old queen, bundling ever closer and raising her temperature, until she died. Succession was assured but the fate of the colony, and the plants and other animals it supported, now rested on the weather.

Fortunately, it was warm and sunny, and the virgin queen took flight. A trail of 9ODA drifted behind her, attracting drones to mate with her. Over several days and repeated flights, the new queen built up a genetic stockpile that ensured the future success of the colony. She was now ready to reign. Every day for the rest of her royal life, the queen laid around 1,500 eggs. Her daily production weighed more than the queen herself and any one of those thousands of eggs could grow up to be a rival. She, herself, would be exhausted, starving and defenceless without an entourage to tend to her every need. She could only trust the most loyal subjects with such intimate and important work. To ensure their devotion, and thereby her position as head of the hive, as well as keep order among the tens of thousands of her subjects, the queen used chemical coercion.

9-Oxo-2-Decenoic Acid

From glands close to her mouth, her majesty exuded queen mandibular pheromone (QMP), a powerful mixture of compounds dominated by 9ODA. Those closest to the queen, the royal retinue that fed, cleaned and cared for her, were exposed to the largest amounts. It ensured their complete devotion and servitude. They would also spread the chemical commands throughout the colony through contact with others in the hive. QMP altered the worker bees' behaviour, it restricted the development of ovaries in everyone but the queen and suppressed the urge to raise new queens. With no thoughts of rebellion, the workers focused on supporting the hive. Flying from flower to flower to collect the nectar needed to feed, the colony also pollinated plants and crops that fed many other species. They worked so industriously that there was enough spare wax and honey for other animals to benefit from their excess.

The queen had a long life producing the eggs that grew into the workers that supported the hive. But, like her predecessor, she could not live forever. As she aged, her output of 9ODA declined and so did her power over her subjects. The old queen was dying. Members of the royal retinue were the first to notice the subtle changes, and they spread the news to everyone else. Freed from their 9ODA suppression, some of the workers started to develop ovaries. They laid their own eggs, raising the drones that would father future generations. Soon there would be a new queen and preparations were being made.

$C_{10}H_{16}N_5O_{13}P_3$

Adenosine Triphosphate
The Zombie

Adenosine triphosphate (ATP) is the currency of energy used by biology. Need some energy for a muscle to contract, for a chemical reaction, or a nerve to send its electrical signal? Simply grab a passing ATP molecule and snap off one or two of the three phosphates from its tail. Reattaching the phosphates is how we store and transfer energy, whether it has been released from respiration, fermentation or photosynthesis. There is no living thing on Earth that does not use ATP, and that is why you need never worry about zombies.

Clambering out of a grave and shuffling about in search of brains requires energy. To get that energy a zombie needs food, hence the search for brains, and also oxygen. That oxygen has to be distributed to cells where it is combined with glucose that has been extracted from the food. In order to do that you need to work the lungs to draw in air, and for the heart to beat to pump it around the body. Dead people do not breathe or have a pulse and therefore no new ATP can be made. But could zombies call on a body's reserves to shamble about and perhaps get more ATP from their victims?

There is not much in the way of ATP reserves in the body, even a living one, because it is simply not practical to store it. To keep a

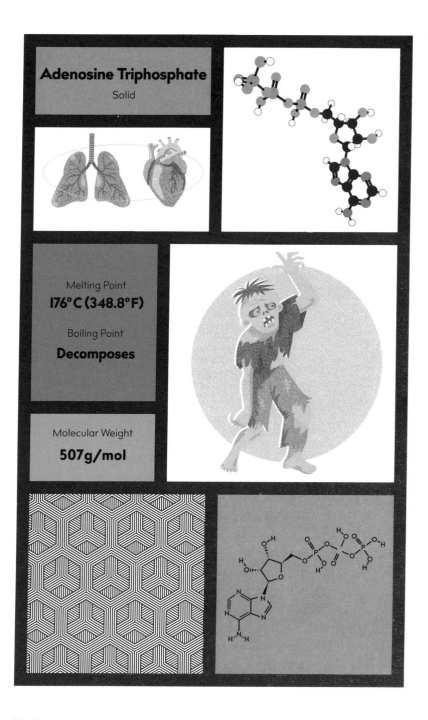

Adenosine Triphosphate
Solid

Melting Point
176°C (348.8°F)

Boiling Point
Decomposes

Molecular Weight
507g/mol

human being going for just a day would require our entire body weight in ATP. Also, ATP dissolves too easily in water – it needs to so that it can move about the body to where it is needed. Instead, there is a relatively small amount of ATP that is constantly broken apart and put back together again. An individual ATP molecule might be unmade and remade thousands of times a day to keep the energy flowing.

The recently deceased may have a little ATP lying around, and the oxygen from their last breath will be used to make a little more. Our bodies also have an emergency backup system where we can continue to produce energy without oxygen. If we are fighting for our lives, or perhaps running away from the undead, our lungs may not be able to suck in enough oxygen to keep pace with the energy we are using in our muscles. Anaerobic respiration is where glucose is broken down in the absence of oxygen. It produces lactic acid and energy that goes into making more ATP. Anaerobic respiration releases much less energy than aerobic, so supplies of ATP will be limited. It perhaps explains why zombies are not the smartest of the many varieties of undead.

Thinking is hard work. Nerve cells are particularly energy-hungry, and the brain contains billions of them. A one-word vocabulary and the ability to be easily outwitted, as demonstrated in every zombie film, are strong indications of a limited mental capacity. Dialling down brain activity may be a zombie survival tactic. Their notoriously slow progress towards their victims may be another way of conserving their limited supply of ATP. And their awkward gait and stiff limbs may be a side-effect of their depleted stocks.

ATP has many roles in the body beyond energy supply. It is involved in sending signals between cells, synthesizing DNA and making proteins. When it comes to muscles, ATP does more than simply release the energy needed to move them. It also acts as a kind of lubricant between the actin and myosin components that make up muscle fibres. When ATP levels drop, as they inevitably do when a person dies, the fibres become locked in place and the muscle stiffens in a process called rigor mortis. In conventional dead bodies rigor mortis is a temporary state. The limbs will become flexible again as the muscles start to decompose.

In summary, should a zombie apocalypse occur, it will be short-lived. But you still need to keep yourself safe for the duration. I would advise against the conventional practice of cutting off the head or destroying the brain – it's messy, unpleasant and unnecessary. Slow zombies should be easy to outrun and, unlike humans, exercise is bad for them. Every shuffling step will deplete their limited ATP until they eventually come to a dead stop. The best thing to do would be to find somewhere secure, have a nice cup of tea and simply wait for it all to blow over.

$$C_{11}H_{12}N_2O_2$$

Tryptophan
The Postprandial Snooze

It can be disconcerting, and a little embarrassing, to wake from a nice nap to find yourself, not in your bed, or even your own home, but looking into the affronted face of your dinner party host. Anyone who has devoted time to planning a convivial evening might expect their guests to at least be able to remain conscious for the duration.

Charged with the crime of a serious lapse in etiquette, you can try to defend yourself by pointing out that dozing after a good meal is not uncommon. Many countries structure their day around a siesta to sleep off lunch and shelter from the hottest part of the day. In the United States, the unconscious state brought about after indulging in Thanksgiving dinner has become known as 'turkey coma'. But the argument that lots of people do it, so it must be okay, may not wash with someone who has spent hours preparing a delicious meal only to be rewarded with snoring. So, for those accused of inappropriate postprandial somnolence, consider applying the tryptophan defence.

Your opening statement should establish the context of your alleged crime. The protein in the eggs, soybeans and meat was broken down into its constituent amino acids in your stomach. Your body then sifted through those amino acids for the twenty that are needed to keep

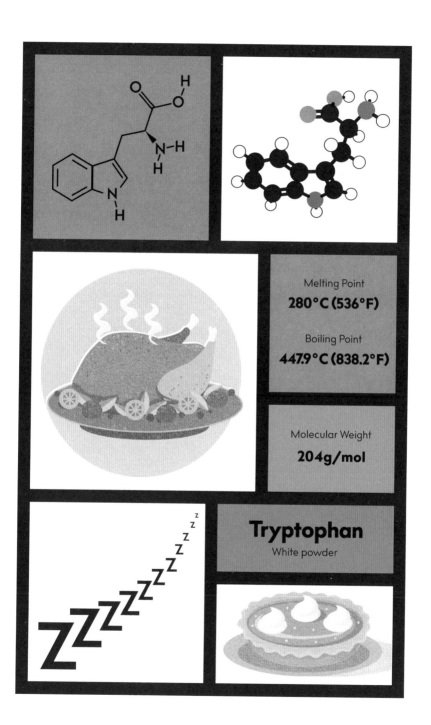

Melting Point
280°C (536°F)

Boiling Point
447.9°C (838.2°F)

Molecular Weight
204g/mol

Tryptophan
White powder

your body healthy. One of those twenty amino acids is tryptophan, the real cause of your mistimed slumber. Unable to make tryptophan for yourself, the sudden influx provided by your host's sumptuous repast caused some temporary biological adjustments. Your body did what every body does with tryptophan: it took some of its molecules and connected them with other amino acids to make proteins. A few more were converted into vitamin B3, which helped you metabolize your meal. And some of the remaining molecules were converted into serotonin, which moved between neurons in your brain to induce sleep. Your napping was not a comment on the quality of the evening, it was chemistry.

Having stated your case, you must be prepared for cross-examination. Tryptophan, the true culprit according to your testimony, is the scarcest of the amino acids. Could something in such small quantities have such a profound effect on your state of consciousness? This is an easy argument to counter. It is well established that tiny changes in the amount of neurotransmitters, like serotonin, even in small regions of the brain, can have big knock-on effects. Your prosecutor is not stupid. They are simply feeding you leading questions.

Tryptophan

How does the tryptophan get into the brain to be converted into serotonin, they ask, when the brain has a very effective barrier for blocking entry to big and bulky molecules like tryptophan. Your answer is that scientists have identified specific proteins that transport amino acids into the brain. This is exactly what your prosecutor expects to hear. Having admitted tryptophan is heavily outnumbered by the other amino acids present in your evening meal, how can it compete for space aboard these transport proteins? This is where you bring in supporting evidence: dessert. Studies have shown that eating carbohydrate-rich foods increases the amount of serotonin in the brain. The sweet dessert your host had prepared, and insisted you had an extra slice of, caused a spike in blood sugar. Insulin released from the pancreas to deal with the saccharides also assisted the uptake of amino acids, except tryptophan. The insulin helped clear the other amino acids from circulation, leaving less competition for those precious places on the protein transports into your brain.

Your argument may be compelling, but it is best to back it up with some mitigating circumstances. Witnesses can be called who counted how many glasses of wine you drank with your tryptophan-laden meal. Extra helpings expanded your stomach and small intestines, triggering feelings of fullness and sleepiness. The parasympathetic nervous system, sensing the influx of food, initiated its 'rest and digest' activities, diverting blood to the digestive system and away from the brain. Alcohol-induced stupor and reduced brain activity may not be flattering, but perhaps show diminished responsibility for your actions.

No one piece of evidence or scientific argument conclusively proves the cause of post-dining dozing, but you will have introduced enough reasonable doubt. The jury of your fellow guests has to weigh the evidence. Even if you escape the maximum penalty of being asked to leave, a community-service sentence (washing up) seems likely.

$$C_{11}H_{12}O_3$$

Myristicin
The Spice of Life

Coveted far and wide for its flavour and flesh-preserving, mind-altering properties, nutmeg could be found in only one place. In one remote, inhospitable land, battered by storms and lacking even in water, it saturated the air with its sweet scent. Whoever had control of the spice would attain such wealth that the difficulties of travelling vast distances to this uncompromising landscape with hostile natives paled into insignificance. The story of the spice trade sometimes reads like a Frank Herbert fantasy without the sandworms. But it is a true tale of greed, war, empire-building and the most powerful company in history.

Ever since ancient Roman times, Europeans have had a strong taste for spices such as pepper, cloves and nutmeg. They made a bland European diet more interesting and helped disguise the flavour of food that was past its best. Nutmeg's main attraction was its sweet scent and flavour. It was also valued as a preservative, and, undeservedly, as a medicine and aphrodisiac. Up until the seventeenth century, nutmeg drifted into Europe through networks of traders. No one was sure where it came from exactly, but it was very far away. The price was inflated at every step of the journey as the quality of the product diminished. Demand, however, never let up. In 1599, news arrived in

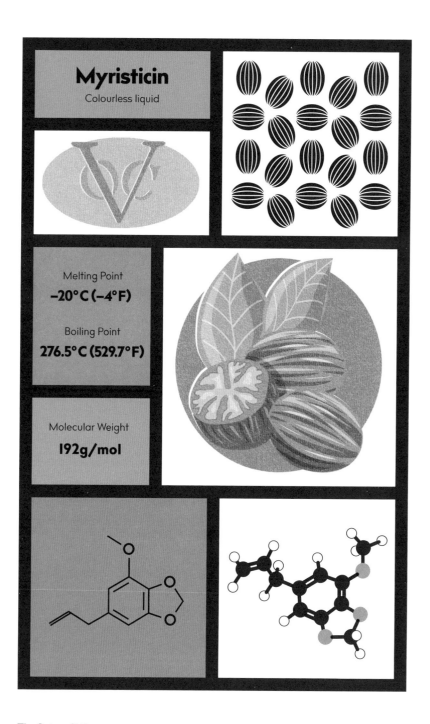

Myristicin

Colourless liquid

Melting Point
−20°C (−4°F)

Boiling Point
276.5°C (529.7°F)

Molecular Weight
192g/mol

Europe that Portuguese ships had landed at the Banda islands, in what is today Indonesia. They discovered that it was here, and only here, that nutmeg was to be found. The smallest island of the group, Run, was the richest in nutmeg. It was also blessed with many deterrents to any outsiders who wished to exploit it. Run was surrounded by ship-wrecking reefs and wracked by terrible monsoons that brought the only fresh water to the island. Then there were the locals, who drove off the Portuguese with a hail of arrows as they tried to build a stronghold.

Undeterred by the Portuguese experience, two great rivals, the Dutch and the British, decided to launch their own expeditions. The hope was to find fast routes to the spice islands and return with shiploads of spice directly to their ports, cutting out the middlemen.

The Dutch decided to form a company of traders, agents and investors that would put up the money, manpower and brutal efficiency needed to dominate the trade. The Dutch East India Company, the VOC, amassed so much power and money it put governments and royalty in the shade. The company constructed ships, set up trading posts, fortifying them and establishing colonies to serve them. It funded armies and determined governorship of those colonies, becoming de facto ruler over them. Trade was encouraged in all manner of goods, but the most profitable by far was spice.

At its trading peak, nutmeg could increase in value three-hundred-fold from source to sale in Europe. The inflated price derived

Myristicin

from several factors. *Myristica fragrans*, the trees that grew the fruit containing the nutmeg kernels, were vulnerable to damage from volcanic eruptions, monsoons or rivals cutting down or burning plantations. Then there was the extortionate cost of transporting spice across thousands of miles of hazardous oceans, and the company's eyewatering profits to be factored in. By the time nutmeg reached its seventeenth-century consumer, not every boy or girl could afford to spice up their life. Nutmeg was reserved for the rich, and even then, its use was restricted to very special occasions such as illness, or Christmas.

Only the fantastically wealthy European could have afforded enough nutmeg to experience its mind-altering properties. Nutmeg contains many compounds, but one, myristicin, is metabolized by the human body into an amphetamine-like substance. It feels like swallowing sandpaper, but a kernel and a half of ground nutmeg can introduce enough myristicin into the body to produce hallucinations, along with nausea, dizziness, anxiety and paranoia. Any feelings of euphoria are followed by a sense of looming death. In Herbert's *Dune*, spice allows some individuals to see the future. For the protagonist, Paul, it brings visions of an impending war. If myristicin had the same powers of precognition, it would have shown a very similar future.

To ensure complete control of the spice trade, the VOC were prepared to go to any lengths – oppression, torture, murder, even decades of war. The peace agreement saw the British concede control of the tiny island of Run. In return, the Dutch handed over New Amsterdam, a small trading centre with fewer than a thousand inhabitants. Today, it is New York.

$$(C_{12}H_{20}O_{10})_n$$

Cellulose
Taking Notes

Cai Lun was a busy man. A senior eunuch in the Han imperial court, his duties included advising Emperor He and overseeing the palace workshop, where instruments and weapons were produced. Cai was also responsible for passing messages between the imperial apartments and the outer court. There were dull notes about day-to-day royal business, and more interesting commissions for artists and scholars to glorify and document the history of the Han dynasty. There was always so much that had to be noted down. And all of it had to be written either on silk or cloth, which was light but expensive, or on bamboo strips, which were cheap but heavy. It was all very inconvenient.

While taking a rest in the palace gardens, Cai watched a wasp hard at work. It buzzed around collecting twigs and leaves, chewed them up into a paste and used it to mould the delicate walls of its nest. Cai had an idea. He gathered bamboo, rags, fishing nets and bark from a mulberry tree, the sort of scraps the wasp might have chosen. Rather than chewing them, he boiled his items and pounded them with stones. He sieved the resulting mush to remove the water, then dried it into flat sheets. The sheets were light and flexible, like the walls of a wasps' nest, and they also absorbed ink, just enough to stick, but not

Cellulose

Odourless, white powdery fibres

Melting Point
270°C (518°F)

Boiling Point
Decomposes

Molecular Weight
342g/mol

蔡倫

so much that fine writing became illegible. They were cheap, easy to transport and store and, most importantly, could be mass-produced.

The royal court tried to keep the secret of paper to themselves, but it was impossible. Paper spread across the Chinese Empire and beyond. By the ninth century it had arrived in the Middle East and, a few centuries later, in Europe. Wherever paper appeared, literature flourished and libraries expanded. It became the preferred material for the written word, displacing papyrus, parchment and vellum. Part of the attraction was that paper needed no specialized materials. Rather than relying on Chinese imports, anyone could make paper for themselves out of whatever wood, cloth or fibrous scraps were to hand. And why? Because they all contain cellulose.

Cellulose is one of biology's basic building materials, formed from thousands of glucose molecules bonded end to end in long chains. Starch is also made of long chains of glucose, but the molecules are linked in a slightly different orientation. It is a subtle difference, but the overall effect is huge. Unlike starch, indigestible cellulose forms flat, straight ribbons that are tough to break. The ribbons pack together side by side and hold onto adjacent threads using hydrogen bonds. Woven into cell walls, these slender strands help plants and bacteria hold their shape in the absence of a skeleton.

These same cellulose strands can be further reinforced with lignin, hemicellulose and other components, to make a substance strong enough to support trees up to 120m (390ft) tall. A tree's height is not limited by the strength of cellulose, but the challenge of pumping water to leaves so high off the ground. Any material that can support the weight of these massive trees while retaining the flexibility that allows them to sway in the breeze is impressive indeed.

Extracting cellulose fibres from everything else they are stuck to is the tricky bit. Harsh conditions are needed. Cai's method of boiling in water and pounding with stone, has been replaced with boiling in water and chemicals such as sodium hydroxide and sodium sulphide. Once freed, the cellulose fibres mat together as they dry.

Cai Lun was not the first person to make paper. The Chinese had been using it for packing since the eighth century BCE, and to write on since the first century BCE, decades before Cai was born. And the story of him being inspired by watching a paper wasp is exactly that. By making small changes, Cai improved the quality of the paper and gave it mass appeal. Over the centuries, his process has been further refined, adapted and mechanized. The cellulose it has produced has been modified and reformed into products he could only have dreamed of.

Cellulose is incorporated into our everyday lives. It holds up the roof over our heads, protects us from the elements and its fibres help move food through our guts. And, thanks to Cai Lun, it can store the sum of human knowledge; our history; our future hopes and anything else our imagination can conjure – even a silly book about molecules.

$$C_{12}H_{22}N_2O_2$$

Nylon
Plastic Fantastic

The invention of the first-ever, fully synthetic fibre was announced with considerable fanfare and some bold claims. According to the press release, nylon had 'the strength of steel and sheerness of cobwebs'. It was not just a cheap alternative to natural fibres like cotton, wool and silk, DuPont's scientists had improved on nature. It was 1938 and the future had arrived. Well, there were still a few technical difficulties, but the future would be along soon.

It had already taken some 230 scientists and technicians more than ten years and $27 million to get to the point of a press release. Coupling one molecule to another is relatively easy, as long as you choose the right combination of atoms to do the coupling. Amine groups had long been known to bond to acid groups. Nature did this all the time, linking amino acids together into protein chains. Get one molecule with an amine group at each end, and another molecule with an acid group at each end, and the two should join hand in hand in an alternating pattern to form continuous polymer chains. The details took some working out, but in 1934, the first viable synthetic fibre was 'drawn'. The scientists criss-crossed the laboratory to see how far it would stretch, covering the space with a giant plastic web.

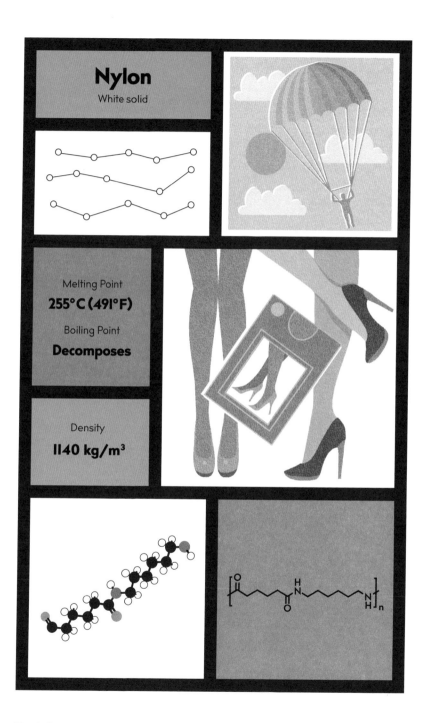

Nylon
White solid

Melting Point
255°C (491°F)

Boiling Point
Decomposes

Density
1140 kg/m³

More experiments were needed to find the best amine molecule to alternate with the best acid molecule to produce a fibre that would not stretch too far or snap too easily. Finding out how to form this new material into fine threads was another challenge. It could not be spun or combed like silk or wool. Instead, it was melted and extruded through tiny holes. Weaving and knitting the new thread into a fabric presented more difficulties – all existing machines were designed to work with natural fibres. But they got there eventually.

Members of the public got their first glimpse of nylon knitted into a pair of stockings in 1939. DuPont's display at the New York World's Fair caused a sensation. By the time nylon stockings arrived in stores the following year, anticipation had reached fever pitch. Women were more than ready for a stocking that did not sag at the ankle and droop at the knee as rayon and cotton stockings did. Silk was expensive and quickly ruined by runs. Nylons were as fine, if not finer, than silk and, though not run-proof, were harder-wearing. Being a thermoplastic, nylon softened on heating. Newly knitted stockings were placed on leg-shaped forms and steamed to heat-set the shape and size. Then, almost as soon as nylon stockings appeared, they vanished again.

In December 1941, the United States entered the Second World War. Nylon followed two months later, when DuPont's entire nylon manufacturing capacity was turned over to the war effort. A nylon flag was hoisted over the White House as a sign of America's independence from Japan and its silk. DuPont adapted its manufacturing processes to make heavier nylon thread to replace parachute silk. Further modifications enabled nylon to be used for more applications. Nylon's strength was perfect for rope. Its light weight was ideal for the nose cones on bombers. Its weatherproof qualities could be exploited for tents. Resistance to moths and mildew made it perfect for everything from uniforms to shoelaces. The military could not get enough.

Until V-J Day, the only nylon stockings available had been from prewar stock. Peace brought a clamour for their return, but technical difficulties meant delays. The 'nylon riots' started in September 1945. Thousands queued outside stores to get to the limited stocks inside, sparking some 'good old-fashioned hair-pulling and face-scratching'. By 1946, the fighting was finally over, and there were enough nylons for everyone.

In the 1950s and 60s, more and more synthetic fibres joined nylon and it expanded into new areas. In 1969, a nylon flag was planted on the moon. Twenty of the twenty-one layers in the moon suits worn by Neil Armstrong and Buzz Aldrin were made from fibres that had originated in DuPont's laboratories. Shops and homes became awash with polyesters and polyamides. Unlike the plastics themselves, the fashions did not last. Synthetics are still with us in blends and specialized fabrics. Nylons, however, remain unchallenged in the hosiery market. The material that caused such a sensation in 1938 is essentially the same product we find in stores today.

$C_{12}H_{22}O$

Geosmin
The Smell of Rain

A long time ago, before humans were even a twinkle in Prometheus's eye, a great war was fought between the gods of Olympus and the Titans. All the immortals took a side. The immense strength and fearsome weapons they fought with inflicted terrible wounds, but no blood was lost. The veins of immortals are filled with golden *ichor*, the ethereal fluid that gives them eternal life, and it soon saturated the ground. The conflict raged for ten long years, until Zeus triumphed and established his eternal reign over the cosmos. But, every time it rains, the earth yields up a reminder of this ancient battle.

Each drop of rain that falls to the dusty ground traps a tiny bit of air between the bottom of the drop and the land. These air bubbles fizz up through the raindrop and burst to release aerosols of scent that drift away on the breeze. This earthy odour has long been enjoyed by humans as a sign that life-giving water is on its way. In 1964, scientists isolated the aroma, a yellow oily substance they named petrichor, a combination of the Greek words *petra*, for 'stone', and *ichor*.

Petrichor has many components; plant oils and the products of creatures living in the soil. However, the earthy notes that humans instantly recognize are primarily due to geosmin, another combination

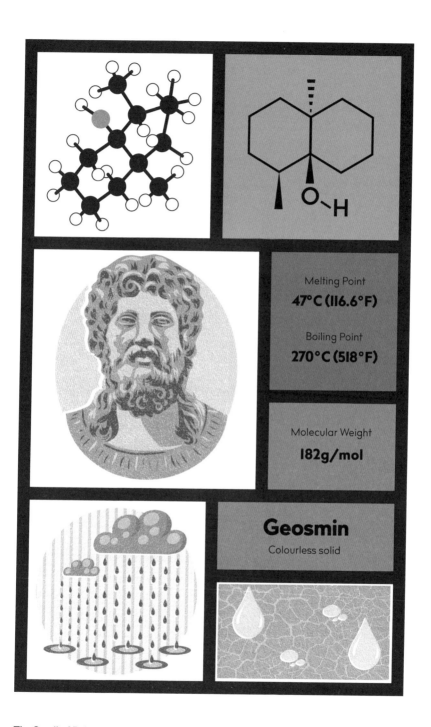

Melting Point
47°C (116.6°F)

Boiling Point
270°C (518°F)

Molecular Weight
182g/mol

Geosmin
Colourless solid

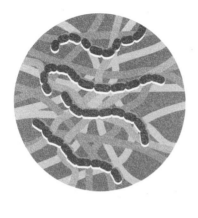
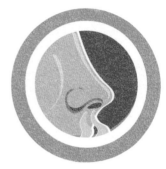

of Greek words, *geo* for 'earth' and *osme* for 'odour'. And the source of this geosmin is involved in another epic battle, this time taking place beneath our feet.

Geosmin is produced by streptomyces, bacteria that live in the soil, where they help break down organic matter. There are more than five hundred different species of streptomyces, but they are all thin, threadlike bacteria that form dense networks. To clear some space to grow into, immobile streptomyces deploy chemical weapons to destroy the many rival bacteria crowding the soil around them. Streptomyces have provided us with more than two thirds of the natural antibiotics we use in medicine, but geosmin is not one of them. It is, instead, a chemical more like the gods' *ichor*.

Unlike the immortals of ancient Greece, no individual streptomyce bacteria can live forever. The best it can hope for is to prolong its life and propagate clones of itself that will live on after it has gone. At the end of a long life of eating and growing and fighting off enemies, an ageing streptomyce will segment itself into a chain of spores, each of which can germinate into a new bacterium if the conditions are right. The geosmin that it releases at the same time improves the spores' chances of survival.

Geosmin attracts springtails, tiny creatures that rummage around in soil and plant detritus. They help disperse nutrients, fungi and streptomyces spores by eating them and excreting them elsewhere.

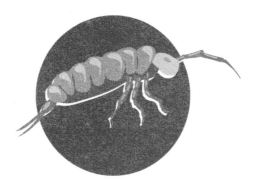

Springtails like damp environments, the ideal spot for a streptomyces spore to start its new life. But, if it is too hot and too dry, the spores will wait it out until more favourable conditions arrive. In a prolonged dry spell, more and more streptomyces will enter the spore stage of their life and more and more geosmin will build up in the surrounding soil. When rain finally falls, petrichor is released in abundance to alert the springtails. And the streptomyces can begin another journey around their life cycle.

The same petrichor flows into our noses and its collection of assorted molecules waft past a tangle of cilia, hair-like protuberances that emerge from specialized nerve cells. If the molecule's shape fits one of the receptors dotted along the cilia, or vibrates against it in the right way (no one is really sure how it works), a signal is generated. Our smell receptors have evolved to detect geosmin at minute concentrations. Rain can be a matter of life and death to all sorts of creatures, not just springtails and streptomyces.

Signals from millions of smell receptor cells are collected in our olfactory bulb before an odorous overview of our surroundings is passed on to the limbic system. This evolutionarily ancient part of the brain has many roles processing sensory information from around the body, as well as being involved in forming memories and processing emotions. It is perhaps why even simple smells can evoke a complex response. The scent of rain can seem fresh and new, while simultaneously creating a sense of nostalgia and triggering old memories believed long forgotten.

$$C_{13}H_{16}N_2O_2$$

Melatonin
Things That Go Bump in the Night

He is the greatest storyteller who ever lived. No one knows so many tales or tells them so wonderfully. He travels ever westwards, silently entering our homes in his stockinged feet as the sun sinks lower in the sky. He dusts our eyes to make us doze and gently blows on the backs of our necks so our heads loll forward into sleep. Our guide on our journey to the land of Nod has many names: Ole Lukøje, the Sandman, Morpheus and melatonin.

We spend a significant portion of our lives doing one activity that is characterized by its inactivity: sleeping. We are regularly physically subdued and mentally disconnected from reality for hours at a stretch. Though we are compelled to visit our private unconscious world every night, no one really knows why. Evolution would not allow us to spend so much time in such a vulnerable state unless it was important. Scientists have proposed theories of sleep as being a time for the brain to relax and wash out the toxins that have built up in the day, as well as an opportunity for the body to carry out some running repairs. What is certain is that, without it, we become ill.

Melatonin
Colourless liquid

Melting Point
117°C (243°F)

Boiling Point
513°C (955°F)

Molecular Weight
232g/mol

Our bodies are pretty good at keeping us to a schedule. Almost every cell inside us has a cycle of chemicals that are built up and broken down over a roughly twenty-four-hour period. But we need to check with the outside world to make sure our internal clocks are not running fast or slow. The movement of the sun through the sky runs like clockwork and the light it sends out can keep us in sync.

Light arrives at the retina, which sends signals via the optic nerve and through the optic chiasm to the body's master timekeeper, the suprachiasmatic nucleus, or SCN, located deep within the brain. The light signals act as a trigger for chemical messages to be sent out to the rest of the body, keeping everything coordinated. As the intensity and colour of the sun's light changes over the course of the day, so do the signals arriving at the SCN. The bright blue component of daylight holds back the production of melatonin, the body's night-time chemical. But, as the sun sets, the blue light disappears and the sky reddens. Melatonin is freed to go about its business of preparing us for what we should do in the dark.

The same old melatonin visits many animals, but they all hear different stories. Nocturnal creatures wake up, energized by his tales. Animals living in the extreme north hear epic yarns that tell them to store fat, thicken coats and hibernate through the long winter. For us humans, melatonin's messages make us sleepy, enticing us away from the preoccupations of the conscious world into dreamy slumber.

The response to melatonin's evening appearance can vary between individuals as well as species. Some take longer than others to succumb to his soporific stories and, as we grow older, we find ourselved less susceptible to his soothing lullabies. Melatonin production decreases as we age. The lenses in our eyes also yellow from the build-up of pigment. As a result, some of the blue light is prevented from reaching the retina. Our natural timekeeper becomes more difficult to read and cues from daylight become less influential. It may be why we go to bed earlier but sleep less in later life.

The world around us has also changed. Humans have learned how to extend their waking hours using light from candles and electric bulbs. These innovations do not stop us from feeling sleepy because the yellow light they produce does not hold back melatonin's progress through our brains. In more recent decades, however, we have switched to LED lights, which, together with the screens of laptops, phones and tablets, illuminate and stimulate us late into the night. The light from these devices, which is blue in tone, has the potential to hold off melatonin and the urge to sleep. We are left with less time to dream because we cannot hold back the sun – as sure as day follows night, the sun appears over the horizon each morning. Daylight streams into our eyes and melatonin is banished from our minds once again. Our night-time escort through the land of Nod disappears with the dawn. If we are lucky, he leaves us one of his stories to remember him by.

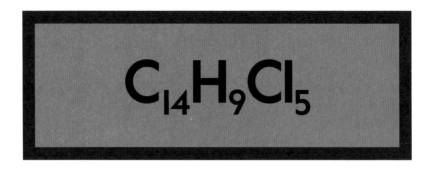

$$C_{14}H_9Cl_5$$

Dichlorodiphenyltrichloroethane (DDT)
Saving the World

This molecule's exploits are the stuff of spy thrillers: a single molecule sent out on government missions to save millions of people from dastardly villains and their fiendish plots. The tick, the flea and the mosquito are the Hugo Drax, Auric Goldfinger and Ernst Stavro Blofeld of the insect world. And dichlorodiphenyltrichloroethane (codename: DDT) was the double-O agent that single-handedly thwarted their evil plans to hold the world to ransom with deadly diseases. DDT has saved more lives than any other chemical. It is undoubtedly a hero but, like James Bond, a flawed one.

Born in 1874, in the experiments of Austrian chemist Othmar Zeidler, DDT found its role in life in 1939. In his search for new insecticides, Swiss chemist Paul Hermann Müller realized DDT's combined talents were perfect for defeating villainous insect foes. The chemical really got on insects' nerves. It provoked them by unlocking sodium channels along the length of the nerve cells. Sodium flowed in, causing the nerves to fire repeatedly until the insect died of exhaustion.

Another strength was DDT's resilience. It could withstand chemical and biological assaults from the environment and remain active for weeks, just as Bond can face a hail of bullets from hordes of henchmen

Dichlorodiphenyltrichloroethane

Colourless crystals

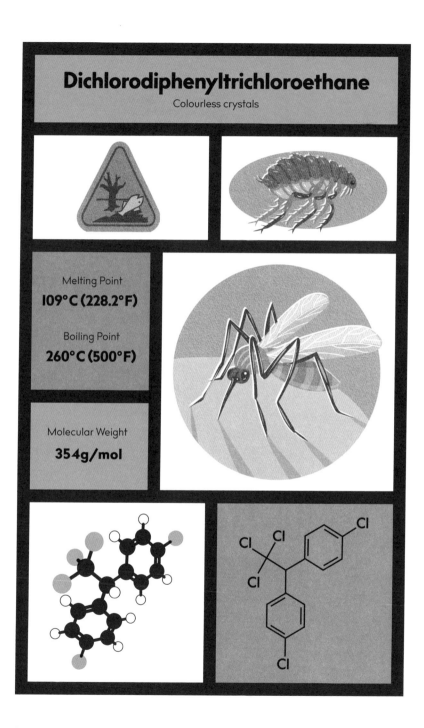

Melting Point
109°C (228.2°F)

Boiling Point
260°C (500°F)

Molecular Weight
354g/mol

and still survive to challenge the big boss in the final showdown. An early test of DDT's abilities came in 1944. *Pediculus humanus*, also known as the body louse, turned up in the recently captured city of Naples, spreading typhus. DDT easily assassinated the louse when all others had failed.

The Second World War ended, but there were still baddies to combat, and DDT was soon promoted to bigger missions. They were not as glamorous as Bond's big-screen adventures, but they were often in exotic locations. In the United States, DDT defeated the Colorado beetle before it could destroy potato crops. It fought off fleas in Ecuador that threatened plague. And in Ceylon (Sri Lanka), DDT came up against its arch-enemy, the mosquito.

The mosquito was the Blofeld to DDT's Bond: a villain with a dozen different plans up its sleeves, or rather in its guts. The mosquito threatened millions of lives across much of the globe with yellow fever, dengue fever and, most terrifying of all, malaria. In the 1940s, Ceylon's mosquitoes spread malaria to two-and-a-half million people every year. DDT was deployed there in 1948. Every home on the island was sprayed regularly for years and by 1962 malaria cases had plummeted to just thirty-one. The World Health Organization (WHO) put together a plan to wipe out the threat of malaria completely, with DDT at the forefront. It appeared to work. Tens of millions of lives were saved. But, as DDT was being cheered as a saviour, criticism and concerns were also being voiced.

Dichlorodiphenyltrichloroethane (DDT)

As 007's exploits have shown, saving the world can involve a lot of collateral damage. DDT was evidently very toxic to insects, but innocent bystanders caught up in its affairs were also harmed by the experience. Fish and birds died from DDT's interactions, and the qualities that had seemed so appealing in the early days began to be problematic. Resilience to damage also meant persistence in the environment and an ability to accumulate as DDT was passed up the food chain. The chemical was found to be everywhere – in soil, in water and in human tissue.

More worryingly, DDT's enemies were becoming familiar with its tricks and taking steps to avoid them. Insects evolved methods of blunting DDT's effectiveness by removing one of its chlorine atoms. It had been the right molecule at the right time; effective, efficient and far less toxic than the arsenic-, lead- and mercury-based pesticides of the past, but the glory days were over.

With hundreds of insect species resistant to DDT, and growing environmental concerns, this chemical agent appeared increasingly out of touch with what a modern pesticide should be. Its use declined and many industrial countries banned it completely. In Ceylon, people stopped spraying homes with DDT in 1964. Five years later malaria cases were back to 1940s levels. Today, DDT still gets sent on sporadic missions in some tropical countries, though its use is heavily restricted.

The WHO had predicted that, by 1963, malaria would be a thing of the past. Fictional secret agents like 007 always save the day, but in the real world it appears the baddie is winning. Bond has been reinvented many times to keep up with new trends and science continues to search for better ways to defeat our common enemies.

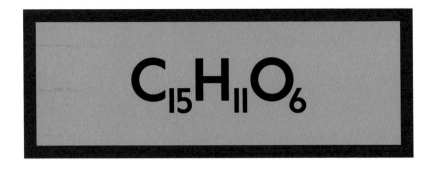

$$C_{15}H_{11}O_6$$

Cyanidin
Colourful Language

The Victorians had a fancy for sending messages to each other disguised in floral bouquets. It allowed the shiest of admirers to declare their true love, and a discreet acceptance or rejection to be made without causing a scene. Volumes were published on the secret language of flowers, but not all the authors of these books agreed on what these flowers were saying. Tansy, for example, could signify resistance, eternal happiness or a declaration of war. Such mixed messaging could be disastrous.

In matters of life and love, it is important to be clear. Plants wanting to perpetuate their species usually cannot do so alone. They must seduce two, often three and sometimes more partners for successful pollination and to spread their seed. Silent, immobile plants cannot run after their heart's desire shouting love poetry. Their partners have to come to them, and they are often trying to communicate their needs to an entirely different class of creature.

For many plants, the answer is to use bright showy colours in their flowers and fruits to entice animals closer. These dazzling displays of different colours are achieved with the sophisticated use of a chemical language. Many different molecules are used to construct these flamboyant messages and, in a clever bit of biochemistry, some

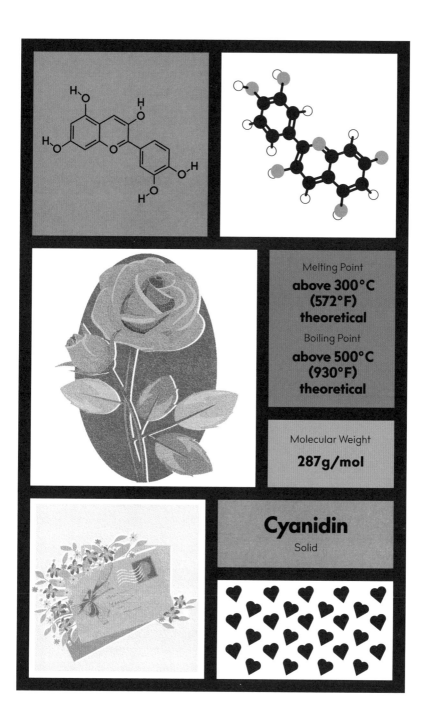

Melting Point
**above 300°C
(572°F)
theoretical**

Boiling Point
**above 500°C
(930°F)
theoretical**

Molecular Weight
287g/mol

Cyanidin
Solid

molecules can be used to give multiple meanings. As the well-known love poem (almost) puts it: 'roses are red and cornflowers are blue'. And the same pigment, cyanidin, is responsible for both.

Cyanidin is a member of the anthocyanidin family of plant pigments. Their name comes from the Greek *antos*, meaning 'flower', and *kyanos,* meaning 'blue', even though they are responsible for the red and purple as well as blue hues of petals and fruits. It is the chemical structure of these molecules that make them colourful. They all have three carbon rings with alternating single and double bonds that can be shuffled about using the energy from light. They also have lots of oxygen atoms dotted around those rings that affect the wavelengths of light that are absorbed, and therefore the colour of the compound. But it is the tiny hydrogen atoms that can be added or plucked from those oxygen atoms that help them put on a particularly colourful show.

In an acidic environment, there are lots of positively charged hydrogen atoms (H^+) floating free. They are attracted to the slightly negative oxygen atoms on a cyanidin molecule, and some of them stick. The result is a rich red colour. As the pH increases and shifts towards neutral, there are fewer H^+ available, causing some of them to detach from the cyanidin oxygen atoms. Without those hydrogens, the compound becomes purple. Push the pH even further and yet more H^+ are lost and cyanidin changes colour yet again, to a greenish blue.

Cyanidin

For a long time, it was thought the difference between a red rose and a blue cornflower was simply the pH of the plant's sap. It turns out it is more complicated than that. Acidity can affect the colour of flowers in hydrangeas, but this is a rare exception. If it were so simple, the elusive blue rose could be made by adding bicarbonate of soda to a vase of red roses. In most flowers, the pigments in the petals and fruits are a complex mix of anthocyanidins attached to glucose molecules, to help them dissolve in water, and stacked together or wrapped up with metal atoms to achieve the perfect hue. But that does not mean that the colour cannot change.

There is more to the colour of a flower than shouting 'look at me'. Not only is the colour tailored to what the pollinating animal prefers, after pollination it can be changed. Altering anthocyanidin concentration, or reshuffling the molecules' arrangement with other components, makes it less noticeable. It can tell a bee, bat or bird that it should move on to a different flower to get their nectar.

Plants also need to attract animals when their seeds are ready to be distributed and not before. Producing more anthocyanidins in the skins of their fruits as they ripen makes a richer red colour. It contrasts strongly with the green leaves, particularly for birds, the main distributors of these seeds, because they are more sensitive to ultraviolet light than humans. The red reflects more ultraviolet than the leafy green backdrop. We humans can still appreciate the colourful language of flowers and fruits, even when the message is not intended for us.

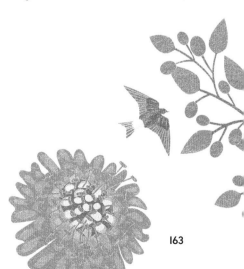

$C_{16}H_{18}N_2O_4S$

Penicillin
True Perseverence

The story of Alexander Fleming's serendipitous discovery of penicillin is well known – how he noticed, in one of the Petri dishes cluttering his bench, that a little spot of mould had killed off the bacteria that surrounded it. And how the penicillin extracted from that mould went on to save millions of lives. A story that is less well known is the one in which Fleming spent four years trying to identify and extract the active component from the mould without success. Whatever it was, it was a very potent killer of pathogenic bacteria. But if it was too fragile to survive the extraction process, it was useless as a medicine. In 1932, Fleming shelved his penicillin work and moved on to other things.

Howard Florey, Ernst Chain, Norman Heatley and their team at the Dunn School of Pathology at Oxford took up the penicillin challenge in the late 1930s. They had a sample of Fleming's *Penicillium notatum* mould, a lot of determination and plenty of ingenuity. Then, just as they were starting to make progress, war broke out. Their work suddenly became much more important and much more difficult.

In between digging bomb shelters, they offered their mould different foods and growing conditions to optimize its growth. They devised elaborate sequences of washes, extractions and separation steps to

Penicillin

Amorphous white powder

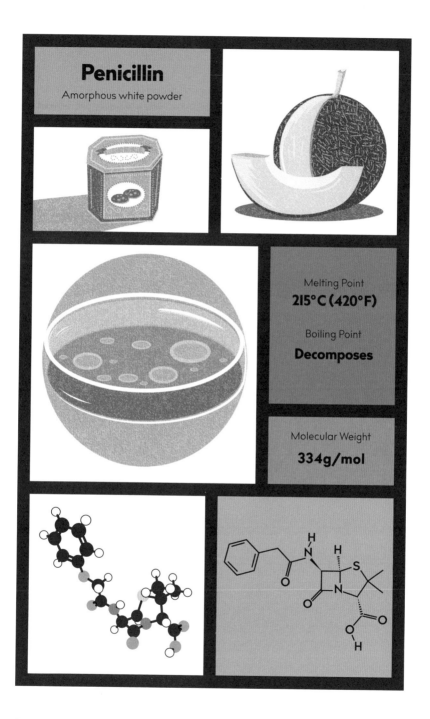

Melting Point
215°C (420°F)

Boiling Point
Decomposes

Molecular Weight
334g/mol

gently tease out the penicillin it produced. All this had to be done using milk churns, bedpans, biscuit tins and anything else they could get hold of in the midst of wartime shortages. But they knew that the results of their efforts, containing just 1 per cent penicillin, were more potent than any other antibiotic available. And, judging by their mouse studies, they had no other adverse effects on the body.

As evidence of penicillin's potential medical benefits mounted, so did the threat of German invasion. The Oxford team worried they would have to destroy their work lest it fall into enemy hands. They rubbed mould spores into their coats knowing they were hardy enough to survive for years and could be used to revive their research if the worst happened. There was no invasion, but there was still a long way to go, both in the war and in their research.

Work continued at a pace. Over Christmas 1940, flasks designed by Heatley, made from ceramic because it was cheap, were stacked, seeded and incubated. By the end of January he had processed 80 litres (140 pints) of crude solution to extract enough partly purified penicillin to try on a human patient. Forty-three-year-old policeman Albert Alexander had scratched his face on a rosebush. The resulting infection had already claimed one of his eyes and it looked like it would claim his life, too. From the first injection of penicillin his condition began to improve. To stretch supplies, penicillin was extracted and recycled from Albert's urine. After one week he was well on the way to recovery and treatment was stopped. The remaining penicillin supplies were given to Kenneth Jones, a one-year-old whose wound had turned septic after a hip operation. Kenneth made a complete recovery. Meanwhile, Albert's infection returned, but the penicillin stocks had been used up. He died just over a month after his first injection. The death was devastating. It showed that treatment had to be continued until the infection was completely gone, even if the patient felt better. It also showed that penicillin was safe for clinical use and had the potential to save many, many lives. The last remaining hurdle was supply, and it was a big one.

No British company could take on the task of scaling up and mass-producing an unknown drug, fully occupied as they were with essential war work. It was American pharmaceutical companies that developed deep tank fermentation technology and discovered a new strain of mould, *Penicillium chrysogenum* from a rotten cantaloupe, that improved the efficiency of penicillin production. Money and resources were ploughed into building up supplies. It was a phenomenal scientific effort, only exceeded in magnitude by the Manhattan Project that produced the world's first nuclear weapons.

In January 1941, there had been enough penicillin to treat one person. By the time of the D-Day landings, in June 1944, there was enough to treat half a million people a month. Now, penicillin's availability is restricted again, but not because of production difficulties. Bacteria have become resistant to its effects, as Fleming warned they would back in 1928. The production of new antibiotics will be every bit as difficult as the first.

$$C_{17}H_{19}ClN_2S$$

Chlorpromazine
Mother's Little Helper

On 19 January 1952, twenty-four-year-old Jacques Lh was brought to Hôpital Val-de-Grâce, Paris. He was severely agitated. This was not his first visit to the psychiatric wing of the military hospital. In the past, medical staff had given him barbiturates, induced an insulin coma and forced electric currents through his brain to shock him into temporary wellness. But these treatments did not always work. Patients like Jacques could became so lost in their mental illness that they could not find their way back. Such people often spent the rest of their lives in the asylum. They were sometimes sedated to give them and the staff some respite, or physically restrained to stop them hurting themselves and others. It was the best the hospital could offer.

By the mid-twentieth century, doctors, surgeons and chemists had made great strides in treating diseases that affect the organs and systems of the body. However, one organ – the brain – was largely ignored. Its sheer complexity was daunting. As the seat of reason and personality, it was clearly very different. And so were the illnesses that it manifested.

New theories and exciting treatments were proposed continuously, and the staff at Val-de-Grâce's psychiatric wing tried them all, more out of desperation than with any expectation of success. The new talking

Chlorpromazine

White, crystalline solid

Melting Point
178°C (352°F)

Boiling Point
205°C (401°F)

Molecular Weight
319g/mol

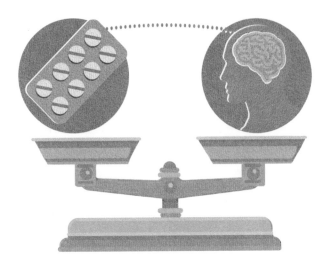

therapy, advocated by so many, could work wonders in private practice, where psychiatrists could spend time with their patients one-to-one. But it was of little use to doctors overseeing hundreds of patients in asylums, especially those too ill to communicate their problems. Staff despaired at how powerless they were to help.

Jacques would likely become just another patient to add to the growing numbers filling the wards of huge asylums that seemed to be popping up everywhere. He would be cared for, or at least cheaply accommodated, like so many others, away from a society that could not cope with them. The conversations in the Val-de-Grâce staff canteen were bleak. Henri Laborit, a surgeon at the same hospital, happened to overhear some of them.

Laborit was interested in reducing the risk of shock, which killed some of his patients during operations. He had been inspired by the recently developed antihistamine drugs. Their main side-effect was drowsiness, not necessarily sleepiness, but a calm detachment. Though undesirable in an antihistamine, it was exactly the quality Laborit wanted for his patients to relax them before surgery. Working with a pharmaceutical company, he tested some of their rejected compounds and found chlorpromazine was just what he was looking for. Deaths on the operating table were dramatically reduced. Perhaps, he suggested to the psychiatric doctors, it might relax their patients too.

Chlorpromazine

So, when Jacques was readmitted that January, doctors reluctantly agreed to try an injection of chlorpromazine. The drug flowed through his bloodstream until it reached his brain. There it blocked the release of dopamine and affected several others of the more than one hundred neurotransmitters that convey messages between the tens of billions of nerve cells housed there. Something tipped the scales of Jacques' mental health back towards equilibrium. He calmed down immediately. Two weeks later he was playing bridge. After three weeks, having received nearly a gram of chlorpromazine in total, he was well enough to leave. Tests on more patients were similarly miraculous. Chlorpromazine cleared their mental fog, made the voices in their heads easier to ignore and gave patients focus. Even catatonic cases were returned to the world. Finally, they could be offered treatment instead of incarceration.

Chlorpromazine was quickly marketed as Largactil – that is, large in action – for its wide-ranging applications, and as Thorazine in the United States. Sales boomed. It spurred the search for more pharmaceuticals to treat psychiatric patients, or anyone who needed a little something to take the edge off the strain of living. Soon Hollywood stars and stressed-out housewives were swallowing pills to get them through the day.

Chlorpromazine was the first drug to show that mental health could be treated chemically, much as physical health could. It was not perfect, and alternatives with fewer dangerous side-effects were soon discovered, but it was still the most effective. It was also no panacea. There is more to mental illness than a simple imbalance of a few key chemicals. Understanding the complexity of the brain remains an enormous challenge for scientists. But, for the millions of people who have been treated with chlorpromazine, it was big step in the right direction.

$$C_{17}H_{19}NO_3$$

Morphine
What's in a Name?

A name can be more than a simple descriptor; it often comes loaded with cultural and historical baggage. Names give layers of meaning and context to our language, but they can also be a minefield of misunderstandings and confusion. Science aims to remove all ambiguity by using concise, carefully defined scientific language.

Chemists have a system for constructing chemical names that describe the exact arrangement of atoms within a molecule. As an example, (4R,4aR,7S,7aR,12bS)-3-Methyl -2,3,4,4a,7,7a-hexahydro-1H-4,12-methano[1]benzofuro[3,2-e]isoquinoline-7,9-diol is a word image of 'morphine'. But it gives no hint of this molecule's long history or how it has influenced society – not even the fact that it is a . . .

Drug *[drŭg]*. Substance used as a medication for the diagnosis, treatment, cure or prevention of disease, or with a marked effect on the structure or function of the body. Origin, Old French *drogue*, a term for the barrels used to keep herbs dry. Many medicines have their origins in plants and herbs and one of the oldest known references of such comes from Mesopotamia. A clay tablet dating back to 3400 BCE lists a dozen recipes and around 250 plant ingredients including . . .

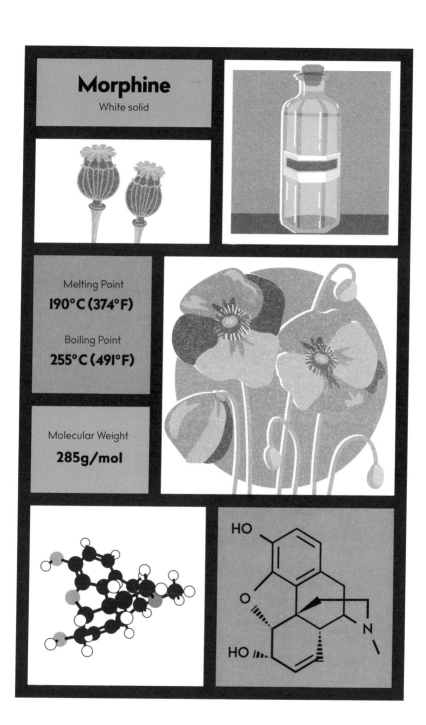

Morphine
White solid

Melting Point
190°C (374°F)

Boiling Point
255°C (491°F)

Molecular Weight
285g/mol

HO

O

HO

N

Hul Gil. Origin, Sumerian, meaning 'joy plant'. Binomial name, *Papaver somniferum*, from Somnus, the ancient Greek personification of sleep. Commonly known as the opium poppy for its sticky sap, released by scoring the plant's seedpod, which can be processed into . . .

Opium *[o'pe-um]*. Origin, Greek *opion*, meaning 'juice'. After a few hours' exposure to the air, the white latex exuded from the poppy head turns into a brown, sticky residue. This is scraped off and shaped into cakes that are boiled to remove impurities. The dried solid residues are then rolled into balls of raw opium. Opium has been used for religious, recreational and medicinal purposes for more than ten thousand years, the most notable historical formulation being . . .

Laudanum *[law'dă-nŭm]*. Origin, Latin *laudāre*, meaning 'to praise'. An opium-based elixir created by Paracelsus in the sixteenth century. He described it as a potent painkiller, but potency could vary because raw opium is an impure substance. It contains a mixture of biologically active compounds classified as . . .

Opiate *[o'pē-ĭ,-āt']*. Compound found within opium or a synthetic derivative that causes an analgesic effect on the body. The quantities and ratios of opiates found in poppies depends on the variety of plant and its geographical origin. Not all opiate compounds produce the same degree of analgesia: noscapine is primarily a cough suppressant; thebaine is a stimulant; and codeine is a moderate pain reliever. The most potent analgesic compound in opium is . . .

Morphine *[mōr'fēn]*. Origin, Morpheus, ancient Greek god of sleep and dreams, son of Somnus. The compound was first isolated from opium by German pharmacist Friedrich Sertürner, in 1804. His experiments revealed its pain-relieving properties, six times more powerful than raw opium, as well as its sedative and euphoric effects. As a pure substance it allowed more precise dosing, but also a quicker route to addiction. Later, chemists made modifications to morphine's chemical structure in efforts to reduce its addictiveness, while retaining its pain-relieving qualities. Replacement of two hydrogen atoms with acetyl groups produced a drug far more powerful than morphine, named . . .

Heroin *[her'ō-in]*. Origin, German, commercial name of diacetylmorphine, chosen to reflect its heroic use in pain relief. The two acetyl groups improve fat solubility and absorption into the brain. Here the acetyl groups are removed, and morphine is reformed to act directly on opiate receptors. Though the analgesic properties are several times greater than morphine, it is also more addictive. Many other compounds that can produce opium-like effects have been identified and invented. They go by the name of . . .

Opioids *[ō'pē-oidz]*. Compounds that act on opiate receptors in the body to produce opiate-like effects. These can include opiates, but also chemically unrelated compounds such as endorphins that are produced naturally by the body, and the synthetic compound fentanyl. Some of these compounds can be hundreds of times more effective than morphine, increasing the risk of overdose because they act as a . . .

Narcotic *[nahr-kot'ic]*. Pertaining to or producing narcosis (insensibility or stupor). Origin, Greek *narkōtikos*, meaning 'benumbing'. The word originally referred to any opiate, but more recently to any drug with effects similar to those of opium. Because of the narrow window between a therapeutic and a lethal dose, legal restrictions have been imposed on the sale and prescription of certain forms of . . .

Drug *[drŭg]*. An illegal substance that causes addiction, habituation, taken for its marked effect on the body.

$$C_{18}H_{10}N_2O_4$$

Melanin
The White Elephant

One night, Queen Maya dreamed a white elephant appeared before her holding a lotus flower in its trunk. It circled around her three times, then entered her womb through her right side. Ten months later, a son was born to Queen Maya, the wisest of all beings, the Buddha. Another white elephant, named Airavata, carries the god Indra, a Hindu deity, and guards his palace. We do not expect to see such magnificent mythic creatures wandering around in our everyday world, but white elephants are not confined to dreams and effigies in temples.

In 1895, a very forthright Englishman was granted the extraordinary privilege of meeting a living, breathing white elephant. He was not impressed. 'The romantic descriptions have no counterpart in reality, and the white elephant himself proves to be more or less a "fraud". He is not all white, but dust coloured.' White elephants are not exactly white, but they are not exactly grey either, and the difference is melanin. This molecule begins with tyrosine, one of the naturally occurring amino acids that make proteins. Enzymes knit tyrosine molecules together, using different stitches and adding embellishments, to make a collection of polymers called melanin. These long strings of modified tyrosine molecules have lots of alternating single and double

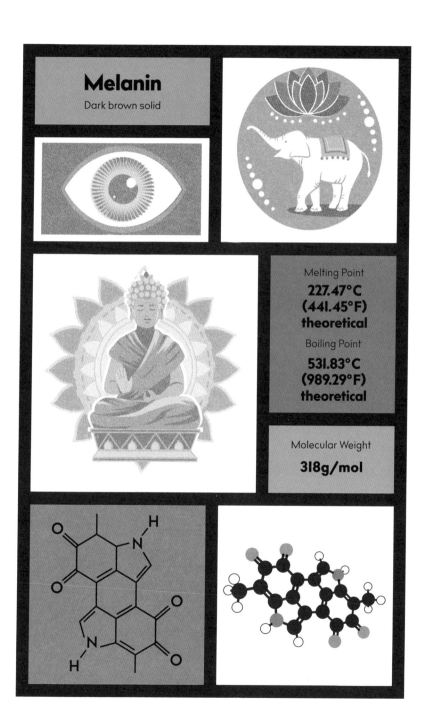

Melanin

Dark brown solid

Melting Point
**227.47°C
(441.45°F)
theoretical**

Boiling Point
**531.83°C
(989.29°F)
theoretical**

Molecular Weight
318g/mol

bonds that can be moved around with the energy from light.
Therefore, these natural polymers take on a range of colours from
yellow, through brown, to black.

Most organisms have at least one use for melanin. In plants, it is
part of the browning of bananas and the colouring of chestnut shells.
In bacteria, it aids their defence against toxic heavy metals as well as
helping to block out damaging ultraviolet light from the sun. In squid
and other cephalopods, manipulating the melanin in their skin allows
them to change colour and camouflage themselves. As a last resort, they
can squirt melanin-filled ink in an enemy's face to block the predator's
view and allow them to escape. In birds, melanin protects feathers from
the wear and tear of abrasion and gives colour to beautiful plumage.
And the list goes on.

In mammals, melanin contributes to hair, skin and eye colour.
It is produced in specialized cells called melanocytes. How busy
these melanocytes are depends on many things, including genetics,
temperature, sunshine and food. How much melanin an animal has
can make a big difference physically, as well as socially. Albino animals
can have any one of a range of genetic mutations that affect how many,
as well as what types of, melanin polymers are produced. Their lack of
melanin gives them pale skin, eyes and hair. As well as an absence of
pigmentation, albinism is associated with deafnesses and problems
with vision. For elephants, albinism means the bright sun can blind
them, and the pinkness of their underlying muscles shows through
their pale skin, making them stand out from the herd. But it can also
mean protection, royal titles and all the ripe bananas an elephant
could ever want to eat.

Melanin

Albino elephants are very rare, but Asian elephants, more so than their African cousins, can display a range of pigmentation. Their trunks and ears, in particular, can show pink patches where melanin is missing. There are, therefore, many different kinds of white elephant. There are the snow-white elephants that appear in the illustrations of Buddhist and Hindu texts. And then there are the pinkish and patchy real white elephants that are grouped into four main categories depending on their particular pigmentation.

In Thailand, white elephants, because of their association with the birth of Buddha, are considered auspicious. They are symbols of wealth, prosperity and royal power. Snow-white elephants have appeared on flags and emblems of the kingdom, and all real white elephants belong to the king. At one time, any white elephant found in the wild had to be presented to the monarch. Some rulers built up a substantial herd of pale, pampered pachyderms.

However, not all white elephants were accepted. Those of the lowest quality might be rejected outright, or instead given as a gift to a courtier who had annoyed the king. Such an impressive gift could not be refused. Nor could such an important elephant be put to work to earn its keep. So, the king would sit back and watch this slightly less than white elephant eat its way through his courtier's wealth. In the West, this story created yet another type of white elephant: something expensive to maintain and difficult to get rid of.

$C_{18}H_{27}NO_3$

Capsaicin
A Question of Trust

Do you trust yourself? Not just the big decisions, but the little things too? We are bombarded with information every second of every day, but in this avalanche of data, how do you tell truth from lies? We constantly filter and prioritize messages, but even the most sophisticated system of evaluation is not foolproof. Weaknesses can be exploited for malicious, entertaining or scientific reasons.

Sensors scattered throughout our bodies register interactions between ourselves and our environment. This raw data is sifted, sorted and channelled through a vast network of nerves to the central nervous system. By processing the assorted messages received, we build an impression of our world, but it can only be as accurate as the information given to us. There are some that seem hell-bent on feeding us misinformation. Capsaicin is one of those tricksters. It sends powerful messages of pain and discomfort, but it is almost all lies. Capsaicin's ability to do real damage is limited, but it is so good at persuading us otherwise that it can be used as molecular propaganda.

To expand their number and advance into new areas, chilli plants must deter those who would threaten their progress without offending potential supporters of their campaign. Capsaicin's message is perfectly

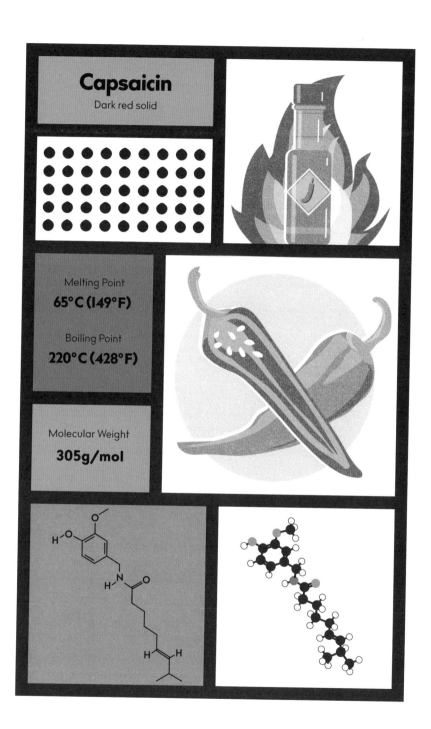

Capsaicin
Dark red solid

Melting Point
65°C (149°F)

Boiling Point
220°C (428°F)

Molecular Weight
305g/mol

tuned to its audience. Birds will swallow any amount of capsaicin's nonsense and carry on helping the plant achieve its goal of spreading its seeds. By contrast, mammals, who do not roam so far and can do more damage to the plants, are scared off by capsaicin's inflammatory chemical rhetoric.

Like a lot of effective propaganda, capsaicin plays on one of our most primal fears. The world can be a hostile place and any creature that wants to survive has to learn to read the warning signs. There is a subset of nerves, nociceptors, that specialize in detecting danger. They are normally activated by things that can harm us – excessive heat, pressure and noxious chemicals – and send out pain signals in response. Capsaicin can convince nociceptors that the temperature is going up, even when it is not. Having different types of nerves explains how animals can differentiate between a range of sensations, such as the warmth of the sun and the pain of a burn. What was not understood until recently, was how these nerves are activated and information about the outside world is gathered. In the 1990s, American physiologist David Julius realized that capsaicin's deceptions could be used to reveal a truth.

Knowing that capsaicin plays a trick on us, Julius decided to find out how the trick is done. He and his team discovered that TRPV1, a kind of protein gate found in nociceptor nerve endings, can be opened by capsaicin, allowing ions to flow into the cell and generate a signal.

Capsaicin

The same protein was found to open at temperatures above 43°C (109°F), when it is hot enough to cause damage to the body.

In 2021, Julius and Armenian American molecular biologist Ardem Patapoutian were awarded a Nobel Prize for their discoveries of the receptors for temperature and touch. Their work was the breakthrough needed to lift the veil on how our bodies acquire information about the world we inhabit. More protein receptors have been identified that respond to different temperatures and pressures, or are activated by different chemicals. The subtle messages these receptors trigger in different nerves gives us our nuanced appreciation of our environment. They also protect us.

Nociceptors are plugged directly into centres that process pain signals quickly and respond automatically. Anti-inflammatory chemicals are produced to minimize damage and the body releases its own chemical propagandists to spin stories about how much damage has been sustained. Endorphins make us feel better and shield us from the worst of the pain. It is this euphoric rush of endorphins behind people's love of spicy food. Some of us like to be tricked. We can also turn those tricks to our advantage. The more we hear capsaicin's angry shouts, the less notice we take. After repeated exposure to capsaicin, nociceptors stop transmitting pain signals and changes to brain chemistry make it easier to ignore the boy who cried wolf. Capsaicin, and knowledge of the receptors it activates, can thereby be used to treat pain.

How we perceive the world is unique to us. Humans are easily tricked, but birds, with different temperature sensors, are deaf to capsaicin's threats. Nobody is perfect, but it is our flaws that make us interesting and tell us most about ourselves.

$C_{20}H_{14}N_4$

Porphine
The Support Staff

Metal atoms are often hailed as the stars of the metalloenzyme show. They tend to be the centre of operations in the reactions carried out by these biological machines. While several metals have unique talents that make them brilliant in their roles, there are many atoms of other elements working behind the scenes. These are the technicians and administrators who keep the enzyme show on the road. Every diva has their personal coterie of assistants, personal trainers, security and stylists to enable them to perform at their best. In the biological world this inner circle surrounding the metal is often a porphyrin.

The simplest of the porphyrins, porphine is the basic framework that defines this chemical family. With its highly symmetric network of carbon, hydrogen and nitrogen atoms, it can form a supportive ring around a metal atom. Its four nitrogen atoms bond directly to the metal, holding it in place and linking it to the rest of the porphine atoms. Electrons and energy flow through these nitrogen conduits. An efficient network of alternating single and double bonds connecting all the porphine pieces ensures a rapid response to the metal's every whim.

The basic porphine structure can be tailored to a metal's needs and the demands of its particular role in life. Add a few carbon, hydrogen

Porphine

Dark red solid

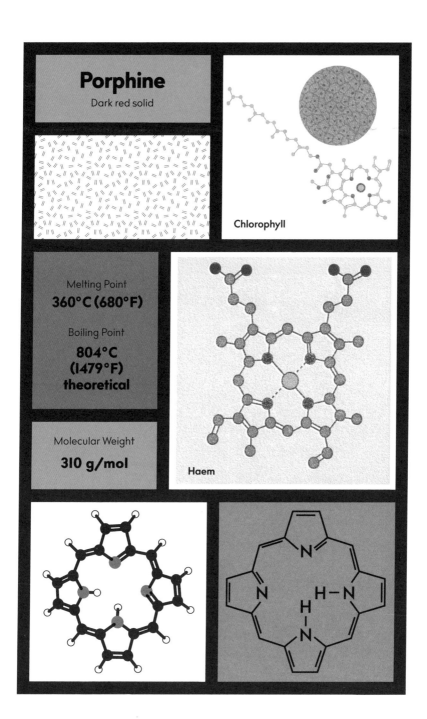

Chlorophyll

Melting Point
360°C (680°F)

Boiling Point
**804°C
(1479°F)
theoretical**

Molecular Weight
310 g/mol

Haem

and oxygen frills and you can host an atom of iron at the centre to make haem. Other embellishments allow a magnesium atom to take centre stage. Then, attach a fancy carbon and hydrogen tail, and you have chlorophyll. Haem and chlorophyll are two of the most important molecules on the planet because together they form the prerequisites for the abundance of life that we see around us. Their roles in respiration and photosynthesis, respectively, form two sides of the same biological coin. Together they keep our planet breathing in and out, day after day. Though the two molecules are very similar, the differences between the metals and their supporting porphyrins allow them to operate in different ways.

Chlorophyll's role is to absorb energy from sunlight and store it in chemicals for later use. The magnesium atom, and the modifications to its porphine support, make chlorophyll green – the best colour to optimize absorption of light from our sun. This biological solar panel channels the energy from the light into freeing and energizing an electron. The high-energy electron is sent off to kick-start a series of reactions, rearranging water and carbon dioxide molecules into glucose and oxygen. When it is all over, the sun's energy has been stored in the chemical bonds within the glucose and oxygen molecules, and an electron is returned to the chlorophyll ready to be recharged.

Reworking glucose and oxygen back into water and carbon dioxide releases energy. Glucose, from food, can be stored in the body. But oxygen cannot be held in reserve in the same way. It has to be captured from the air and transported to the site where it is needed on demand. Once delivered, the two molecules must be combined to release their energy in manageable chunks. This is respiration, a complex process that involves iron at every step. And without the porphyrin supporting the iron, it would rust to a halt.

Iron has a fierce addiction to oxygen. It is perfect for grabbing hold of oxygen molecules from our lungs. But bare, naked iron atoms would not let go of their oxygen once they had hold of it. So, our body surrounds each iron with a supportive porphyrin to make haem, and wraps that up in a protective protein coat to make haemoglobin. When the time comes for iron to release oxygen, the protein helps the separation and the porphyrin holds onto the iron in a tight hug. Haemoglobin delivers oxygen to the next stage. Again, iron is involved, complete with its porphyrin. This time the haem is incorporated into cytochrome enzymes. Here, the porphyrin supports the iron as it loans and receives electrons that are shuttled back and forth, facilitating the break-up of oxygen and release of its energy.

Whether it is magnesium in chlorophyll, iron in haem or cobalt in vitamin B12, without their porphyrin network, these metals would soon go off the rails. Icons, stars and divas are fantastic. The world would be a dull place without them. But they, and we, are nothing without our support networks.

$$C_{20}H_{24}N_2O_2$$

Quinine
The Conquistador

The story of quinine is one of colonialism. Malaria's empire stretches over vast geographical regions and has subjugated billions of humans. Quinine started a resistance movement against this brutal regime. Its acts of sabotage diminished malaria's power and pushed back its frontiers. But it also enabled other empires to grow.

At some point in the distant past, at least thirty million years ago, the malaria parasite got together with the mosquito. The insect's interior was a comfortable place to set up a temporary home and that home travelled around, carrying the parasite to new places. When humans first emerged a few million years ago, the opportunity arose for malaria to expand into new territories.

Malaria soon established a successful plan for human colonization. At first, the parasites set up a base of operations in the liver. Starting with a small outpost, they settle in, multiply and make preparations for expansion. On reaching sufficient numbers, the parasites spread out along a pre-existing transportation network – the circulatory system. Then, in a coordinated attack, they raid the red blood cells in search of food. The parasites gorge themselves on the haemoglobin they find inside, devouring the nutritious protein and spitting out the toxic

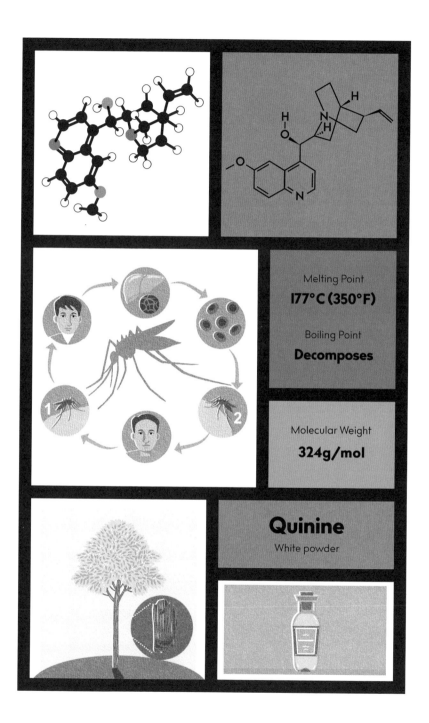

Melting Point
177°C (350°F)

Boiling Point
Decomposes

Molecular Weight
324g/mol

Quinine
White powder

haematin bones. The colonizers grow stronger, mature and multiply until they rip the red blood cells apart. Meanwhile, the colonized are ravaged by chills, fevers and violent paroxysms. Sometimes the damage can be enough to destroy malaria's new home completely. In most cases the unwilling host is left wrecked, but intact. The invaders can float free in the blood plasma waiting to be collected by a passing mosquito so the cycle can start again in a new host.

When humans first walked out of Africa, they carried the malaria parasite with them into new lands. Over time humans have changed their landscape to make themselves more comfortable through agriculture and permanent settlement, unwittingly also improving the lives of malaria's great allies, mosquitoes. By the sixteenth century, malaria's empire stretched across Africa, Europe and Asia. Kings and commoners were felled to maintain malaria's grip over vast swathes of humanity. Pockets of resistance emerged through genetic mutations giving some populations protection against infection. But the parasite was about to meet much stronger opposition.

Malaria sailed to the New World with smallpox, measles and the conquistadors. The humans that met them had never faced enemies

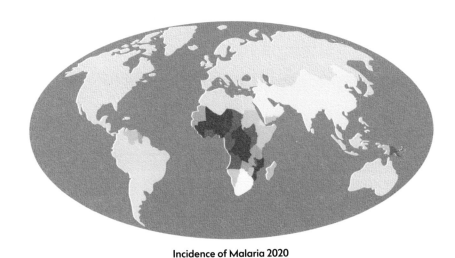

Incidence of Malaria 2020

0   10   25   50   75   100   200   300   400

like it and they were crushed under their combined attacks. But the proud Incas refused to bow down to malaria. They had their own innovative weapons fashioned from the bark of the quinaquina tree. Along with gold and silver, tonnes of quinaquina bark, later renamed cinchona, were shipped back to Europe. The secret weapon it contained was identified as quinine. Extracted and refined into a precision weapon, quinine became the first chemical to be used as a specific cure for a disease.

Quinine hits the malaria parasite where it hurts, in its food supplies. Though the details remain obscure, quinine either hinders haemoglobin digestion, or causes the parasite to choke on the toxic haematin bones. Perhaps both. However it works, quinine represented the first major challenge to malaria's empire and its dominions shrank. As Europeans increased their hold over South America, malaria's grip on Europe began to weaken. West Africa, however, remained one of the parasite's strongholds. The people who lived there had learned to live with the parasite the hard way. Thousands of years of death and illness had toughened their genetic resolve against invasion. It also, inadvertently, protected them against other invaders. Without the same natural defences, European slave traders armed themselves with quinine to set up outposts on the African coast. From there twenty million Africans were transported to the New World. Quinine supplies were too scarce and too expensive to allow the white man to venture any further into the continent's interior. Africa was known as the white man's grave until the 1880s when prices and availability afforded quinine's deployment on a scale that supported mass colonization.

Quinine's sabotage techniques worked, but they came at a cost. Potentially lethal side-effects saw the drug being replaced by safer synthetic alternatives. The malaria parasite has adapted effective defences against these new attacks, but has been much slower to catch on to quinine's tactics. Quinine still has a role to play in the battle to overthrow malaria's domination, but the war is far from over. Malaria still holds sway over vast regions and peoples, claiming around half a million lives every year.

$$C_{20}H_{28}O$$

Retinal
Let There Be Light

Navigating a path through life is tricky. Organisms have developed many different ways to gain information about their environment, including touch, sound, taste and, of course, sight. Our world is flooded with light, which we use to gather information about our surroundings. Reflected light can show us threats and obstacles or wonder and opportunities. We all see the world a little differently, yet, chemically speaking, we all see it in the same way.

Retinal is the molecular switch that turns on the lights in the biological machinery of sight. This simple molecule is composed of a chain of carbon atoms linked together in an alternating pattern of single and double bonds along its length. A single bond is like an axle, with the atoms free to rotate, like wheels, at either end. A double bond is like putting a stick between the spokes, locking the wheels in place. The retinal molecules in the rod and cone cells of our eyes are held in a specific shape using these double bonds. The double bond roughly in the middle of the chain locks the molecule in a bent shape. It looks and behaves like a light switch in the off position. If a photon of light hits the retinal switch, it is absorbed and breaks the middle double bond, or removes the stick from the spokes. The atoms, or wheels, at the ends of

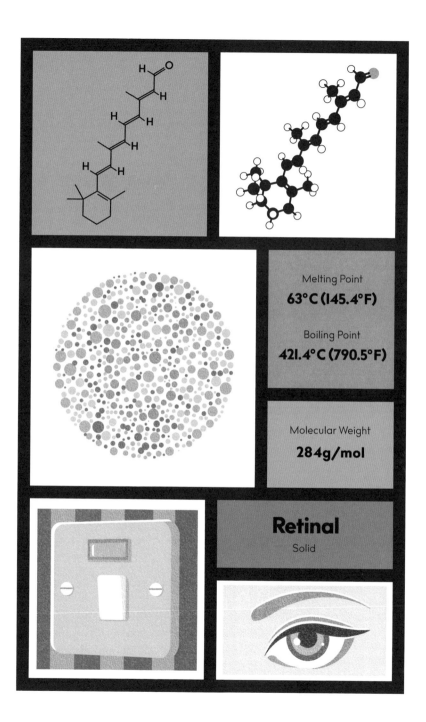

Melting Point
63°C (145.4°F)

Boiling Point
421.4°C (790.5°F)

Molecular Weight
284g/mol

Retinal
Solid

the remaining single bond are now free to turn, and the bent molecule twists and straightens. The switch is flicked to the 'on' position and the double bond re-forms to hold it there.

A switch needs to be connected to something to be useful. The retinal switch is connected to a second molecule by a handy oxygen atom at the end of its carbon chain. This second molecule is a protein, called an opsin, that provides the link to the rest of the visual system. The physical movement of retinal, from bent to linear, kicks against the opsin and triggers a cascade of chemical changes. The process transforms the absorbed light into an electrical signal that is transmitted along nerves to the brain.

Switching the lights on is easy, but switching them off is harder. The straightened retinal has to be detached from its opsin by an enzyme and moved into the dark before other enzymes can twist it back into its bent configuration. The 'off' switch is then reattached to an opsin and is ready to go again. It may sound convoluted, but it is an excellent setup. Retinal's rapid response to light and the big physical change is a quick and clear signal. And the stability of the 'off' shape in the dark means we are not dazzled by false signals. Retinal is the ideal molecule for a light switch. It is even easy to make.

We make retinal from vitamin A. Some of our food contains vitamin A ready-made, and some contains the raw ingredients. Two molecules of vitamin A can be manufactured from a single beta-carotene molecule

Retinal

by snapping it in half and making a simple chemical modification. Beta-carotene is an orange pigment found in several plants, including carrots. It is the kernel of truth behind the propaganda that eating a lot of carrots will help you see in the dark. A deficiency of vitamin A certainly can lead to night blindness, and eating carrots, or other beta-carotene-containing foods, will prevent this very debilitating condition.

Vision is such a useful way of sensing the world, evolution has reinvented it several times. But it has always converged on the same combination of retinal tethered to opsin. Whether you are a mammal, bird or fish, it is retinal that captures the light needed to see. Only insects and some marine animals have made minor changes to this molecular switch because it is so well suited to the task. What we see, however, is tailored to each species' needs. The opsin tunes the retinal to absorb a narrower range of wavelengths of light. And, like all proteins, opsin is made according to the DNA instructions within an organism. Genetic variation means different animals make different versions of the protein, meaning that bees see ultraviolet and dogs do not see green. The electrical signals the opsin triggers can also be interpreted by the brain in a range of ways. We all have the same visual system, but our perception of the world is unique to us.

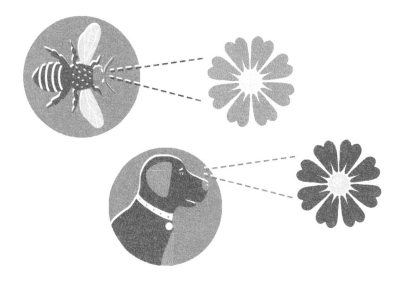

$$C_{21}H_{30}O_2$$

Progesterone
Women's Lib

Use this basic recipe for a stock contraceptive as a foundation for sexual revolution. Popular with millions of women around the world, it forms the basis for many varied dishes. Do not substitute cheaper ingredients. Some have used lead compounds in place of yams; though effective, it leaves a toxic aftertaste. Others have added herbs with unreliable results. If short of time, instant, high-quality, pre-cooked versions are widely available. Consult your doctor to get the right brand for you.

Ingredients

• A selection of risks from childbirth; once common, these are now harder to find, but not obselete
• A variety of difficulties providing for a large family; widely available
• Numerous restricted career options; availability varies, check locally
• One women's rights campaigner (Margaret Sanger)
• One philanthropist (Katharine McCormick)
• A handful of scientists – a good mix of biologists and chemists
• Lots of yams (*Dioscorea mexicana* or 'Cabeza de Negro' work best)
• A squeeze of oestrogen for seasoning

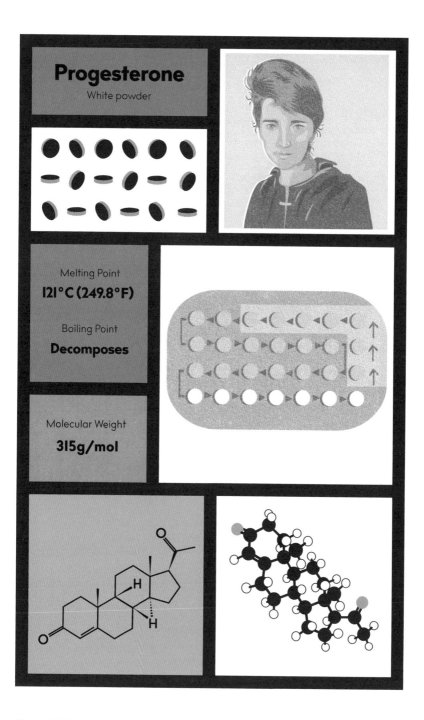

Progesterone
White powder

Melting Point
121°C (249.8°F)

Boiling Point
Decomposes

Molecular Weight
315g/mol

Preparation

1. Take the risks of childbirth, the difficulty
of providing care for a large family and
restricted career options, and allow
them to foment into a deep desire to
control fertility. Check the results carefully
– everyone has their own preferred taste.
Try not to add too much salt.

2. Prepare your women's rights campaigner by training her in nursing.
Then expose your Margaret Sanger to poor families struggling to cope
and to women so desperate not to have another child that they are
willing to risk their lives with illegal abortions. Sanger's anger will add
spice and her fearless practical work in promoting family planning will
give a robustness to the dish. A dash of Katharine McCormick adds
richness to the flavour. Leave them to simmer in the background.

3. Use some 1930s biologists to identify and isolate the sex hormones,
the oestrogen and progesterone family of compounds responsible for
secondary sexual characteristics and regulating the reproductive cycle.
Keep some oestrogen aside for later. Separate out progesterone, the
compound that prepares the womb and Fallopian tubes for pregnancy.
Marinade it in the knowledge that women do not ovulate during
pregnancy. This compound, a steroid structure based on four fused
rings of carbon at its heart, will form the stock structure from which
to build your final revolution. Set aside for the duration of the
Second World War.

Progesterone

Cooking

4. The amount of progesterone available from
the prewar methods of preparation are tiny. Skim off the
details of progesterone structure and activity and discard the rest.

5. Take the yams and mix in Russell Marker, a chemist, to transform
the plant steroid diosgenin from the yams into progesterone. Add the
chemist Luis Miramontes, to make progesterone into the more potent
norethisterone. Check consistency with biologist Gregory Pincus.

6. Having confirmed the norethisterone will inhibit ovulation,
reintroduce Margaret Sanger and turn up the heat. Transfer the whole
mix to Rio Pedras, Puerto Rico, to ensure a balanced blend of flavours.
(Please note, the original taste-testing procedure, though standard for
1955, was not ideal. If recreating this today, you will require a larger
group of volunteers and more stringent ethical and practical methods
to avoid overlooking any bitter flavours that have been introduced.
These include breakthrough bleeding, thrombosis and migraine.
Add in a tiny squeeze of oestrogen to counteract some of these.)

7. The recipe is not perfected, but it works and, with a clear appetite
for this new addition to the menu, it is ready to be served. From 1957,
it can be dished out as a menstrual regulator. Leave a little longer, and
it will be acceptable, and extremely popular, as a contraceptive.

The balance of ingredients has been modified over the years. Initially
the recipe produced such a rich flavour not everyone could stomach
it. Worldwide, it has become known as not just any pill, but The Pill.
It has been used as a base to extend education, create new career
opportunities and sweeten family life.

$$C_{26}H_{23}N_4$$

Mauveine
Fifty Shades

In the mid-nineteenth century, chemistry went through a notable purple patch. Lurking within the pitch-black depths of coal tar, chemists discovered the ingredients for a rainbow of colourful chemicals. And what had been a waste product was shown to contain wealth fit for an emperor. A modest mauve heralded the start of the modern chemical industry. Fashion, pharmaceuticals and chemistry would never be the same again.

By the turn of the nineteenth century, chemistry had shaken off its murky alchemical past. It was now a respectable and professional science, but it was not a very profitable one. The first few decades of the new century were littered with exciting chemical discoveries. Chemists earned many awards, but little in the way of money. It is understandable that when George Perkin's son William expressed an interest in the science, he was instead steered towards a career in architecture. But, the teenager's obvious talents, and some persuasive words, convinced his father to enrol him at the Royal College of Chemistry under the esteemed tutelage of August Hofmann.

Hofmann challenged his student to synthesize quinine, the only effective drug for the treatment of malaria, which, at that time, was

Mauveine

Black solid

Melting Point
**259.73°C
(499.51°F)
theoretical**

Boiling Point
**600.91°C
(1113.63°F)
theoretical**

Molecular Weight
391g/mol

only available from South American cinchona bark. William's starting point would be coal tar, a by-product of the coal gas industry. The industry considered it worthless and would give away huge barrels of it free to anyone who asked. But coal tar was rich in hydrocarbon compounds, which had the potential to form the basic framework for much more complex molecules, like quinine.

Of the roughly ten thousand compounds to be found in coal tar, young William singled out aniline to use in one of his experiments. His chemical manipulations yielded a 'perfectly black product', not the colourless quinine he had hoped for. Nevertheless, he persisted with what most chemists would have poured down the drain. He purified his perfect black, dried it and chemically digested it to produce a purple compound that he used to stain a piece of silk. William noted that neither washing nor sunshine faded the brilliant, lustrous colour.

Purple is not just another colour; it is dye royalty. Legend has it that Hercules's dog bit into a mollusc he found on the beach at Tyre and it stained his mouth the colour of coagulated blood. The *Murex brandaris* and *Murex trunculus* molluscs, found along the Mediterranean coast, produce a pigment that became known as Tyrian purple. Thousands of molluscs had to be milked, and the mucus put through a complicated process to dye a single robe. Purple was pricey. The Phoenicians became rich and purple became the colour of royalty and those in high office.

The eighteen-year-old William decided to patent his purple dye and go into business manufacturing it, though many tried to discourage him. The dye industry had plenty of natural dyes and centuries of experience working with them. No one would be interested in a new shade of an existing colour in an untried formulation. But, George Perkin, who had been so sceptical at the start, along with his sons, sank their personal savings into building a factory to produce William's purple on an industrial scale.

The newly formed company was helped considerably by their dye's royal associations. When Empress Eugénie, wife of Napoleon III of France, was spotted sporting a mauve dress, everyone went crazy for the colour. Often called Perkin's purple or aniline purple, the Perkins themselves adopted the French name mauve and, in his scientific papers, William described his novel chemical compound as mauveine. Whatever it was called, people could not get enough of it.

Mauve, however, proved to be a fleeting fashion. Many other chemists were soon transforming black coal tar into a riot of colourful dyes. And they stained not just cloth, but different bodily tissues and bacteria. Aniline dyes have made their mark as analgesics, such as antifebrin, and led to azo dyes, a family of chemicals that includes the sulfa drugs and the first antibiotic, prontosil. William failed to make quinine, but he kick-started an industry that would go on to produce many other antimalarial drugs, some derived from the chemicals he had industrialized years earlier. Indirectly, his work has advanced and improved products as diverse as food, perfume and explosives.

The chemical industry, founded on colourfast dyes, boomed. Its founder, however, faded from public view. Thanks to his family's early support, William's curiosity and industry enabled him to retire a wealthy man at the age of just thirty-six.

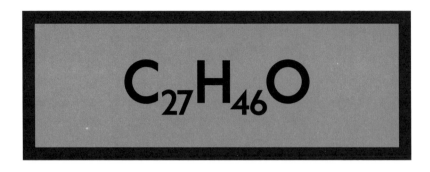

$$C_{27}H_{46}O$$

Cholesterol
Mr Duplicitous

Comparing a compound to a god might be seen as a compliment, but compliments can be backhanded and gods are not always good. Cholesterol has been described as a Janus-faced molecule, after the two-faced Roman god of duality, passageways, doorways, beginnings and endings. Like the god, cholesterol has many contradictory qualities. It helps things flow and puts up barriers. It greases the wheels and clogs up the system. It keeps us alive, but it can also bring about our untimely end.

Cholesterol is a complex molecule created from very simple starting materials. A two-carbon acetate group is added to, twisted around and fused together over thirty-nine biological steps into four fused fatty rings with a greasy tail and an alcohol head. It may not sound like a healthy arrangement of atoms, but the body would not go to so much trouble to make it if it was not good for something. And cholesterol is good for a lot of things.

Chemically, cholesterol is the starting point for the steroid hormones that control sex changes and the fertility cycle. It is also involved in metabolism and inflammation. With a little help from sunlight, cholesterol can be converted to vitamin D, which keeps our bones healthy and strong. It also has some useful physical properties.

Cholesterol

White or faintly yellow solid

FOE

FRIEND

Melting Point
148.5°C (299.3°F)

Boiling Point
360°C (680°F)

Molecular Weight
387g/mol

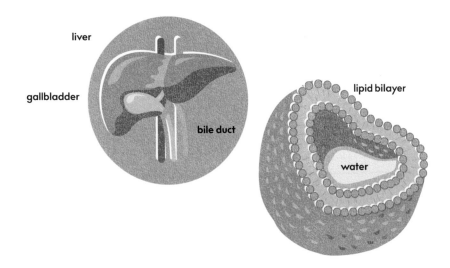

Every cell in our bodies needs cholesterol's physical presence. To keep the contents of a cell from spilling out, they are contained within a membrane. This membrane is made of a lipid bilayer, an oily skin that surrounds the watery contents like a soap bubble. To prevent this bubble popping too easily, cholesterol is included. The alcohol group at the head of the molecule pokes out into the watery surroundings, but the waxy bulk of its body squeezes in among the lipids, or fat, in the bilayer. It helps these lipids pack together more tightly, but still allows them to shift and stretch as the body moves.

As an effective insulator, cholesterol is packed into the myelin sheaths that coat nerve cells. It helps isolate the electrical signals generated within the cell from the conducting environment without. Our brains, packed with nerves, have a huge demand for cholesterol to keep us thinking clearly. It makes up around 17 per cent of the solid weight of the brain. Though every cell in the body is capable of making cholesterol, most is produced in the liver and transported to where it is needed.

Moving a waxy molecule through a watery body is not easy. To help it dissolve in the bloodstream, it is wrapped up in water-soluble proteins. The surface of these proteins also comes with molecular keys that lock into receptors on cells that determine how the cholesterol is distributed around the body. Some proteins carry cholesterol away from the liver, and some transport it back.

In the liver, cholesterol is converted into hormones or other useful compounds such as bile acids. Cholesterol and bile acids are sent to the gallbladder where they are stored and concentrated until mealtime. When our chewed and part-digested dinner empties out of our stomach and starts its lengthy journey through our small intestines, it is given a squirt of bile to help it on its way. The bile neutralizes the stomach acid, helps the fatty and oily parts of the food emulsify with the watery parts and assists their journey through the gut wall and into the body. A lot of the cholesterol and bile acids are absorbed along with the dietary fats so they can be cycled round again.

This flow of cholesterol compounds around the body works well until something gets stuck. Then, the properties that make cholesterol so useful turn against it. The ability to pack fat molecules more efficiently, as cholesterol does in cells, can also mean that too much cholesterol in bile can pack together with calcium salts and bile pigments to make gallstones. It was this high concentration of cholesterol in one inconvenient place that enabled its discovery in 1784.

Cholesterol's insolubility in water that helps form an effective barrier in cell membranes can also cause it to clog our arteries. The build-up of fatty deposits in our circulatory system can narrow the path blood has to flow through and bits can break off to cause blockages elsewhere. High levels of blood cholesterol are associated with increased risk of heart disease and stroke. Cholesterol could be accused of duplicity, but cholesterol might argue it is just a victim of circumstance.

CHOLESTEROL

$$C_{257}H_{383}N_{65}O_{77}S_6$$

Insulin
The Good Manager

The problem of diabetes mellitus is a significant one. It has held humans back for thousands of years, restricting growth and curtailing output. If humankind were a company, diabetes would have warranted several awaydays and idea showers. Many theories have been thrown in the wok to see what sizzles. Humankind Incorporated has even followed a seven-point strategy to try to solve the problem. The resolution has come through teamwork, good communication and delegation, all the things management try to instil in us through those dreaded team-building activities. Let us drill down a little deeper.

Detection: The first written account of the disorder comes from the second century. Aretaeus of Cappadocia used the term *diabetes*, Greek for 'siphon', to describe a condition characterized by weakness, thirst and excessive urination.

Logging: Further incidents were documented and in more detail. In the eleventh century, Avicenna's account noted that a sufferer's great thirst resulted in copious amounts of 'wonderfully sweet' urine; they became very hungry, but rapidly lost weight despite eating well. In the

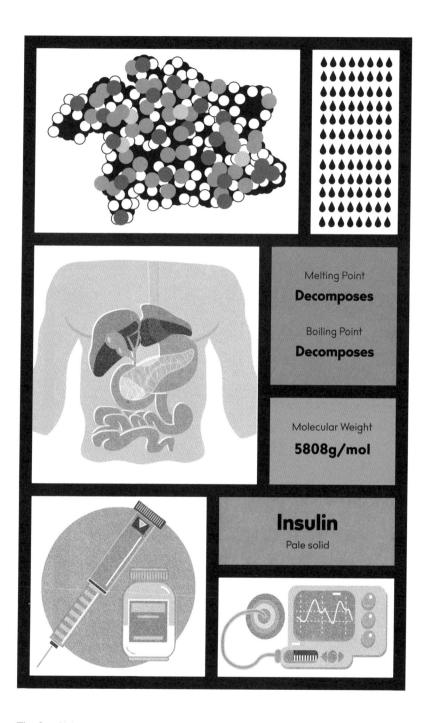

Melting Point
Decomposes

Boiling Point
Decomposes

Molecular Weight
5808g/mol

Insulin
Pale solid

seventeenth century, Thomas Willis added the Latin word *mellitus*, 'honey sweet', to more accurately describe the disease. In the eighteenth century, Matthew Dobson found sugar in the blood, as well as urine, indicating diabetes was not a kidney problem. In the nineteenth century, Edward Sharpey-Schafer determined that the pancreas, specifically the islets of Langerhans, produced the substance that metabolized sugar and called it 'insuline'.

Diagnosis: From the evidence obtained, it is time to get our ducks in a row. Diabetes mellitus is a serious metabolic disorder; an inability to metabolize glucose causes sugars to accumulate in the blood. Large quantities of glucose-rich urine are excreted to flush it out. The body compensates for its lack of energy by consuming its fat reserves, resulting in wasting.

Workaround: The idea of supplying insulin from an external source led to attempts to give pancreas extract by mouth, but this did not give relief. An alternative method was tried in 1921. Frederick Banting and Charles Best, working in John Macleod's laboratory at the University of Toronto, prepared extracts from the islets of Langerhans and injected them into a diabetic dog. The dog, which moments earlier had been close to death, sat up and wagged its tail. With help from J.B. Collip, more pancreatic extracts were prepared and more diabetic dogs injected successfully. The first human to receive their pancreatic extract was thirteen-year-old Leonard Thompson, who was dying of diabetes in Toronto General Hospital. With regular injections of insulin, he was able to return home. Twelve months after its first isolation, insulin was commercially available, due to dire need and the more relaxed rules around approving medicines in the early twentieth century.

Error record: For more than fifty years, the demand for insulin was met using supplies extracted from cows and pigs. These were largely successful but, as demand increased, so did the number of allergic reactions. In 1969, Dorothy Crowfoot Hodgkin determined the structure of human insulin, having worked on the problem for thirty-five years. She showed it was a relatively small protein made of two chains, one containing twenty-one amino acid residues and the second containing thirty. Bovine and porcine insulin differs by only a few amino acids, but it is enough to make a difference.

Resolution: Fifty-one amino acids may be a small number by protein standards, but it is too many to synthesize easily in a chemistry lab. It was time to think outside the box. Genentech, the first-ever biotechnology company, founded in 1976, took a left-field approach. It decided to outsource the task of human insulin synthesis to bacteria. In a brilliant piece of interspecies delegation, a common language was used to incentivize *Escherichia coli* bacteria into producing insulin in bulk. The DNA instructions for human insulin were synthesized and introduced into the E. coli genome. As the bacteria grew, they followed the DNA instructions and produced insulin, even though they had no use for it. The insulin could then be isolated and formulated for injection. The first genetically engineered drug was approved for human use in 1982. But this is still only a replacement for what diabetics cannot make for themselves

Closure: The low-hanging fruit has been harvested, but there are still big prizes to be won. The problem of diabetes will only be ended when the fault in the islets of Langerhans can be corrected so diabetics can produce their own insulin for themselves.

$$C_{6760}H_{10447}N_{1743}O_{2010}S_{32}$$

Botulinum Toxin
The Fountain of Youth

The search for the secret of eternal youth has been long. We have not found a way to cheat death, but we have devised many tricks to try to give that impression. All sorts of chemicals have been smeared, swallowed and injected in efforts to slow down the signs of ageing or cover over the cracks. It is ironic that one of the planet's most deadly known substances is used to make us look young and keep us healthy.

People go to extraordinary lengths to fool others into believing they are further from their grave than they really are. For much of human history, some have been willing to pay a high price in terms of internal damage to make them look good on the outside. In the past, faces were painted with white lead make-up and blemishes were banished with arsenical face washes. With increasing scientific knowledge, it might be expected that the shift in skin care would be towards using less toxic ingredients. In fact, twentieth-century medicine, in full knowledge of its lethal potential, recommended one of the most feared bacterial poisons for cosmetic use.

The deadly nature of this bacteria was realized as early as the nineteenth century, when several outbreaks of food poisoning produced some unusual symptoms and a high mortality rate. Rather than the

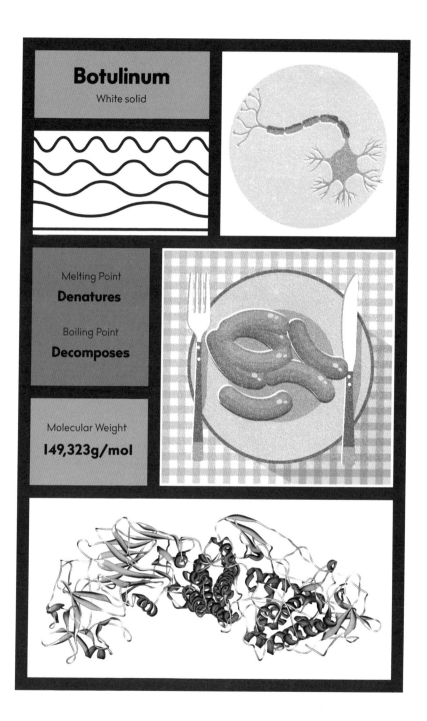

Botulinum
White solid

Melting Point
Denatures

Boiling Point
Decomposes

Molecular Weight
149,323g/mol

usual vomiting and diarrhoea of food poisoning, these victims also had blurred vision, difficulty swallowing and muscle weakness that, in some cases, paralysed people to the point where they could not breathe. A common factor linking these cases appeared to be sausages, so when German physician Justinus Kerner first described the condition, he named it botulism, after the Latin for sausage.

The problem was not the sausages, however, but the bacteria *Clostridium botulinum* growing within them. In order to clear a path of colonization through spoiled sausage and other foodstuffs, the bacteria produces a toxin. Botulinum toxin can rip through proteins, including human ones, and specifically the proteins involved with sending messages from nerves to muscles. Chemical messengers, neurotransmitters, are released from nerve endings to dock at adjoining muscle cells, telling them what to do. These neurotransmitters are held in vesicles inside the nerve cell until it fires, triggering proteins to release them. With the proteins disabled, the neurotransmitters become trapped. No matter how strong the signal, the message simply is not passed on and the muscle does nothing.

By the 1970s, controlled doses of purified botulinum toxin were being used deliberately to block signals to specific muscles. Jean Carruthers, a Canadian eye specialist, injected tiny doses of the toxin around the eyes of her patients to treat their squint. The muscles would relax and the eyes would realign. When her patients returned for a check-up, she noticed that the wrinkles in the skin around their eyes had faded. As our body's outer covering, the skin has to face whatever the world throws at us. It keeps us together, shields us from everyday harm and is still flexible enough to allow the muscles underneath to move us through life. Skin performs its tasks brilliantly, but the daily abuse takes its toll and our skin loses its elasticity over the years. The accumulation of frowns and laughs eventually leave their mark. Stopping the muscles from folding and creasing the skin prevents those worrying wrinkles, but is it worth the risk?

Botulinum toxin is thousands of times more potent than white lead or the arsenic compounds used in Victorian skin-care products, but it is not deadly sausage poison that has been banned from cosmetic use. Understanding what these compounds do inside the body, and how the body responds to them, means risks can be managed.

The damage inflicted by lead and arsenic is too widespread and long-lasting for them to be considered safe. Botulinum toxin has very specific targets, however, and over a period of months the body can rebuild the broken pieces. It means further injections are needed to maintain the smooth facade, and you can also recover the more lived-in look if you change your mind.

With a history of safe medical use behind it, controlled doses and protocols for safe use, botulinum toxin was re-branded as botox and launched in the cosmetic industry in the 1990s. And it continues to find new medical applications, from relieving painful muscle spasms, to treating chronic migraines. We still cannot cheat death, but we can use some of its tools to make living more comfortable.

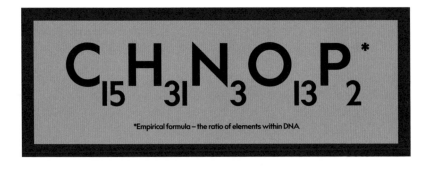

Deoxyribonucleic Acid
The World Dominator

Deoxyribonucleic acid (DNA) may be the most successful molecule of all. Starting from very humble beginnings in a muddy puddle four billion years ago, it has gone on to achieve total world domination. DNA is the chemical language of life. This molecule documents all the information needed to build and run an organism. It is written in a script so simple any cell, animal, vegetable or bacterial, can read it. But it is a language we still struggle to understand.

Life, in all its infinite variety, can be described in a language of only four letters – A (adenine), C (cytosine), G (guanine) and T (thymine). These letters represent chemical units, called bases, strung together in a specific order along a sugar and phosphate backbone to form biological words and sentences. One long line of DNA script is paired up with a second, like two sides of a zip. Just like the teeth on a zip, each A base is perfectly shaped to match T, and C pairs up perfectly with G on opposite strands. The zip is closed and held tight by hydrogen bonds formed by hydrogen atoms bridging the gap between nitrogen and oxygen atoms on opposite bases. The locked strands twist and curl into a neatly packed compendium of information about an organism.

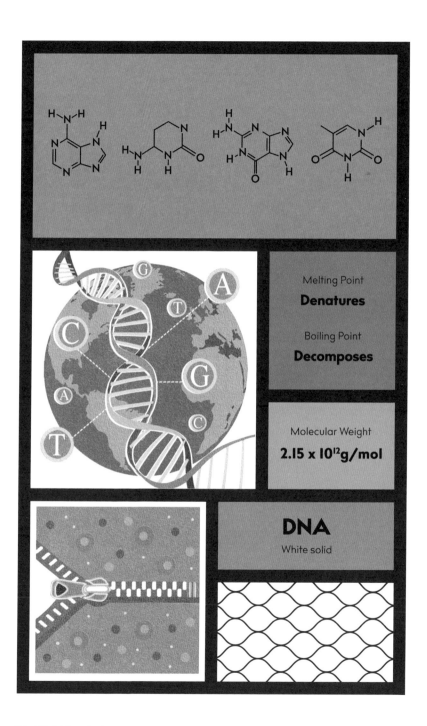

Melting Point
Denatures

Boiling Point
Decomposes

Molecular Weight
2.15 x 10^{12}g/mol

DNA
White solid

Virtually every cell in every living thing carries a complete copy of its DNA instruction manual around with it for reference. Some cells store this information in a central library, the nucleus, for safe keeping. In humans, the DNA library is usually separated into forty-six sections, called chromosomes. Each chromosome contains genes, like individual books on specific topics. They can be long or short, but each gene is a discrete sequence of bases that describes a single piece of biological information, such as instructions on building a protein.

The cells in our body are specialized to perform some tasks and not others. Cells in our retinas do not need to make insulin and cells in the pancreas do not need to make proteins to detect light. Inside each nucleus, the chromosomes are organized so that the parts that are not called on so often are tucked away, and commonly used genes are easy to access. But that still leaves reams of text to scan through to find the necessary information for that cell. DNA's four bases can be used to spell out not just the genes themselves, but also markers to identify and locate genes, as well as promotional material to encourage more frequent use of some genes over others. But, even after tracking down the gene needed for one of the cell's tasks, the information cannot be removed. The books in this genetic library are not loaned out.

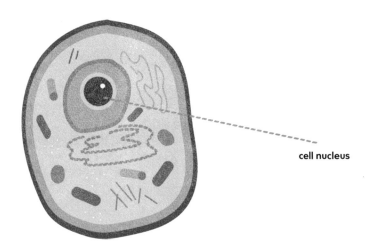

cell nucleus

Deoxyribonucleic Acid

The hydrogen bonds that hold the double-stranded DNA together are weak enough to be unzipped so the single lines of script can be read and copied. Transcribing the text of a single strand of DNA is easily done by matching each base with its pair and writing a new complimentary second strand. More combinations of the four bases are used to punctuate the text, showing where to start and where to stop copying. These transcriptions can then be removed from the nucleus and taken to parts of the cell where they are translated into proteins. The original text is left intact and ready to be read again and again.

The genes, the books coding the instructions for the rest of the body, take up relatively little of the total volume of DNA. Just as a library houses original texts, there are far more volumes devoted to commentaries and criticisms of those texts. Our DNA is loaded with non-coding DNA. What was once believed to be junk, obsolete books and tatty old scraps of text that evolution had not bothered to clear out, may in fact be there to help interpret and regulate the genes.

Like any good writer, biology has used a few simple chemical building blocks to create a complex language full of nuance, double-meaning, emphasis and understatement. The four bases in DNA, just like letters in a written language, can be accented and punctuated to give meaning. That this same language, admittedly with a few dialects, grammatical variations and colloquialisms, is used by every form of life on Earth is mind-blowing. Scientists have been able to read the text of life for some time, but it will take many more years to understand it.

The Periodic Table

Period 1	H							
2	Li	Be						
3	Na	Mg						
4	K	Ca	Sc	Ti	V	Cr	Mn	Fe
5	Rb	Sr	Y	Zr	Nb	Mo	Tc	Ru
6	Cs	Ba	Lu	Hf	Ta	W	Re	Os
7	Fr	Ra	Lr	Rf	Db	Sg	Bh	Hs

Lanthanides	La	Ce	Pr	Nd	Pm
Actinides	Ac	Th	Pa	U	Np

		11	12	13	14	15	16	17	18
									He
				B	C	N	O	F	Ne
				Al	Si	P	S	Cl	Ar
		Cu	Zn	Ga	Ge	As	Se	Br	Kr
		Ag	Cd	In	Sn	Sb	Te	I	Xe
		Au	Hg	Tl	Pb	Bi	Po	At	Rn
		Rg	Cn	Nh	Fl	Mc	Lv	Ts	Og

Gd	Tb	Dy	Ho	Er	Tm	Yb	Lu
Cm	Bk	Cf	Es	Fm	Md	No	Lr

Bibliography

Akhavan, J. 2015. *The Chemistry of Explosives*, 3rd Edt. RSC Publishing, Cambridge.

Anson, G., Walter, R. 1748. *Voyage Around the World, in the Years MDCCXL, I, II, III, IV.* J. M. Dent & Sons Ltd., London.

Atkins, P. W. 1995. *Molecules*. W. H. Freeman & Company.

Ballantyne, C. 2007. Does Turkey Make You Sleepy?: Stop Blaming the Bird for Your Turkey Daze. *Scientific American*. https://www.scientificamerican.com/article/fact-or-fiction-does-turkey-make-you-sleepy/

Ban, T. A. 2007. Fifty Years of Chlorpromazine: A Historical Perspective. *Neuropsychiatric Disease and Treatment*, 3(4): 495–500.

Berber, N. N., Lechevalier. 1965. Geosmin, an Earth-Smelling Substance Isolated from Actinomycetes. *Applied Microbiology*, 13(6): 935–938.

Berry, M. D. 2004. Mammalian Central Nervous System Trace Amines. Pharmacologic Amphetamines, Physiologic Neuromodulators. *Journal of Neurochemistry*, 90: 257–271.

Block, E. 2010. *Garlic and Other Alliums*. RSC Publishing, Cambridge.

Braun, S. 1996. *Buzz: The Science and lore of Alcohol and Caffeine*. Oxford University Press, Oxford.

Brown, M. S., Goldstein, J. S. 1985. A Receptor Mediated Pathway for Cholesterol Homeostasis. *Nobel Lecture*, December 9.

Caterina, M. J., Schumacher, M. A., Tominaga, M., Rosen, T. A., Levine, J. D., Julius, D. 1997. The Capsaicin Receptor: A Heat-Activated Ion Channel in the Pain Pathway. *Nature*, 389: 816–824.

Coady, C. 1993. *Chocolate: The Food of the Gods*. Chronicle Books.

Cook, G. The Science Behind Pyrex Glass. Corning Museum of Glass, https://pyrex.cmog.org/content/science-behind-pyrex-glass

Deuber, C. G. 1936. Effects on Trees of Illuminating Gas in the Soil. *Plant Physiology*, 11(2): 401–412.

Emsley, J. 1993. What Lurks Within that Nasty Niff. *The Independent*. https://www.independent.co.uk/news/science/

molecule-of-the-month-what-lurks-within-that-nasty-niff-methyl-mercaptan-causes-halitosis-and-smelly-socks-but-it-also-has-industrial-uses-says-john-emsley-1473122.html

Emsley, John. 1998. *Molecules at an Exhibition: The Science of Everyday Life*. Oxford University Press, Oxford.

Emsley, J. 2006. *Vanity, Vitality, and Virility: The Science Behind the Products You Love to Buy*. Oxford University Press, Oxford.

Garfield, S. 2002. *Mauve: How One Man Invented a Color That Changed the World*. Norton & Company, New York.

Gandhi, M. 2002. *The Essential Gandhi: An Anthology of His Writings on His Life, Work, and Ideas*. Vintage Books, New York.

Gratzer, W. 2002. *Eurekas and Euphorias: The Oxford Book of Scientific Anecdotes*. Oxford University Press, Oxford.

Gregory, A. 2018. *Nodding Off: The Science of Sleep from Cradle to Grave*. Bloomsbury Publishing Plc, London.

Hager, T. 2008. *The Alchemy of Air: A Jewish Genius, a Doomed Tycoon, and the Scientific Discovery That Fed the World but Fuelled the Rise of Hitler*. Three Rivers Press, New York.

Hager, T. 2019. *Ten Drugs: How Plants, Powders, and Pills Have Shaped the History of Medicine*. Abrams, Inc., New York.

Hall, N., Lister, E., Johnston, J., Osborne (III), C. 1999. *The Age of the Molecule*. Royal Society of Chemistry.

Handley, S. 1999. *Nylon: The Manmade Fashion Revolution*. Bloomsbury Publishing Plc, London.

Henderson, P. 2009. Sulfur Dioxide: Science Behind This Anti-Microbial, Anti-Oxidant, Wine Additive. *Practical Winery & Vineyard Journal*, January/February. https://web.archive.org/web/20130928111625/http://www.practicalwinery.com/janfeb09/page1.htm

Hicks, J. 2010. The Pursuit of Sweet. *Science History Institute*, May. https://www.sciencehistory.org/distillations/article/pursuit-sweet

Hobhouse, H. 1986. *Seeds of Change: Five Plants That Transformed Mankind*. Papermac.

Inglis, L. 2018. *Milk of Paradise: A History of Opium*. Pan Macmillan, London.

Jarriault, D., Mercer, A. R. 2012. Queen Mandibular Pheromone: Questions that Remain to be Resolved. *Apidologie, Springer Verlag*, 43 (3): 292–307.

Karpenko, V. Norris, J. A. 2002. Vitriol in the History of Chemistry. *Chem. Listy*, 96: 997–1005.

Klompan, U., Wootvatansa, N., Kanjanapimai, K., Ariyatugun, K., Pantakod, P. 2018. 'White Elephant' the King's Auspicious Animal. *JHSSRRU*, 20: 361–372.

Kovarik, W. 2005. Ethyl-Leaded Gasoline: How a Classic Occupational Disease Became an International Public Health Disaster. *Int. J. Occ. Environ. Health*, 11: 384–397.

Kurzer, F. and Sanderson, P. M. 1952. Urea in the History of Organic Chemistry. *Journal of Chemical Education*, 33(9): 452–459.

Lax. E. 2005. *The Mold in Dr. Florey's Coat*. Owl Book, New York.

Lecerf, J.-M., de Lorgeril, M. 2011. Dietary Cholesterol: from Physiology to Cardiovascular Risk. *British Journal of Nutrition*, 106: 6–14.

Luo, D-G., Xue, T., Yau, K-W. 2008. How Vision Begins: An Odyssey. *PNAS*, 105(29): 9855–9862.

Metaye, R. 2022. LiFePO⁴ Battery (Expert Guide on Lithium Iron Phosphate). *ClimateBiz*. https://climatebiz.com/lifepo4-battery/

Miodownik, M. 2013. *Stuff Matters: The Strange Stories of the Marvellous Materials that Shape Our Man-Made World*. Penguin UK, London.

Moon, R. O. 1931. Van Helmont, Chemist, Physician, Philosopher and Mystic. *Proceedings of the Royal Society of Medicine*, P. 23–28.

Nicolaou, K. C., Montagnon, T. 2008. *Molecules That Changed the World: A Brief History of the Art and Science of Synthesis and its Impact on Society*. Wiley-VCH Verlag GmbH.

Noever, D. A., Cronise, R. J., Relwani, R. A. Using Spider-Web Patterns to Determine Toxicity. *NASA Tech Briefs*, 19(4): 82.

Porter, R. 1999. *The Greatest Benefit to Mankind: A Medical History of Humanity from Antiquity to the Present*. Fontana Press.

Price, R. 2010. *Man Made Magic: When Science Meets Fashion*. MX Publishing, London.

Regnier, F. E., Law, J. H. 1968. Insect Pheromones. *Journal of Lipid Research*, 9: 541–551.

Romeo, J., Wärnberg, J., Nova, E., Díaz, L. E., Gómez-Martinez, A. and Marcos, A. 2007.

Moderate Alcohol Consumption and the Immune System: A Review. *British Journal of Nutrition*, 98: S111–S115.

Schaller, G. E. 2012. Ethylene and the Regulation of Plant Development. *BMC Biology*, 10:9.

Smith, G. 2021. *Overloaded: How Every Aspect of your Life is Influenced by your Brain Chemicals*. Bloomsbury Publishing Plc, London.

Snow, M. D. 1847. *On the Inhalation of the Vapour of Ether in Surgical Operations: Contains a Description of the Various Stages of Etherization, and a Statement of the Result of Nearly Eight Operations in which Ether Has Been Employed in St. George's and University College Hospitals*. John Churchill, London.

Snow, S. J. 2008. *Blessed Days of Anaesthesia: How Anaesthetics Changed the World*. Oxford University Press, Oxford.

Stimpert, J. 2000. Ira Remsen: The Chemistry was Right. *The Gazette, The Newspaper of the John Hopkins University*, 30(2).

Stone, E. 1763. An Account of the Success of the Bark of the Willow in the Cure of Agues. *Philosophical Transactions*, 53: 195–100.

Stone, T. and Darlington, G. 2000. *Pills, Potions and Poisons*. Oxford University Press, Oxford.

Wald, G. 1967. *The Molecular Basis of Visual Excitation*. Nobel Lecture, December 12.

White Junod, S., Marks, L. 2002. Women's Trials: The Approval of the First Oral Contraceptive Pill in the United States and Great Britain. *Journal of the History of Medicine*, 57: 117–160.

Witt, P. 1954. Spider Webs and Drugs. *Scientific American*, December, P80-86.

Yeung, A. S., Ivkovic, A., Fricchione, G. L. 2016. *The Science of Stress: What it is, Why We Feel it, How it Affects Us*. Ivy Press, Brighton.

The Nobel Assembly at the Karolinska Institutet has today decided to award the 2021 Nobel Prize in Physiology or Medicine jointly to David Julius and Ardem Patapoutian for their discoveries of receptors for temperature and touch. Press release from *The Nobel Assemble at Karolinska Institutet*, 4 October.

Tearless Onion Created in Lab Using Gene Slicing. *Science Daily*. 2008. https://web.archive.org/web/20161124025149/https://www.sciencedaily.com/releases/2008/02/080202115345.htm

About the Author

Kathryn Harkup is a former chemist turned author. Her first book was the international best-seller *A is for Arsenic*. She has also written about the science of Frankenstein in *Making the Monster*, all the ways to die in a Shakespeare play in *Death by Shakespeare* and looked into the science, plots and tech in the world of James Bond in *Superspy Science*. Her prequel to this book, *The Secret Lives of the Elements*, was published by Quercus in 2021.

Acknowledgements

First, special thanks must go to Kerry Enzor and Quercus for letting me write about even more chemistry. I have huge appreciation for Anna Southgate's talents at steering the whole project and making my scribblings much better than they deserve to be. Luke Bird's brilliance can be seen on every page he has designed along with Jo Parry's excellent illustrations. Thank you to all of them.

Many people have helped with ideas and wrangling my words into a much more readable and enjoyable form. My parents, Margaret and Mick, have been a huge moral, emotional and proofreading support, as they always are. Justin Brower, Sharon Harkup, Matthew May, Richard Stutely, James Whiting, Mark Whiting and The Marmalades: Odette Brady, Jodie Eastwood, Julia Graves, Gary McCullough, Atika Shubert. They have all given welcome feedback and support. And, last, but by no means least, Bill Backhouse has been fantastic at supplying tea and a sympathetic ear when needed. Any remaining errors, bad phrasing or incomprehensible references are all my fault and mine alone.